APPRAISAL & ASSESSMENT
IN MEDICAL PRACTICE

A Practical Guide for Management and Staff

Appraisal & Assessment

IN MEDICAL PRACTICE

A Practical Guide for Management and Staff

J.W. Rodney Peyton

TD BSc MSc(Educ) MD FRCS(Eng,Ed & I) FRCP(Lon) PGDL

2000 MANTICORE EUROPE LIMITED

First published in Great Britain in 2000 by Manticore Europe Limited
Silver Birches, Heronsgate, Rickmansworth, Herts. WD3 5DN

Printed and bound in Great Britain by J.H. Haynes & Co. Ltd., Yeovil

British Library Cataloguing in Publication Data
A CIP record for this book is available from the British Library
ISBN 1 900887 06 1

This book supports programmes in Appraisal and Assessment
developed by The Royal College of Surgeons of England

Acknowledgement

I should like to acknowledge and thank my colleagues who have assisted me with this project: to Dawn Haydock, Christine Irwin and Cherith McWilliams, my thanks to them for typing and retyping the manuscript; to John Templeton, Liam McCaughey and Myrtle Richardson for reading the proof and giving me their opinions on the content and finally to the team at the education department of the Royal College of Surgeons of England for their support. Also to Richard Warman for reading the manuscript and helping to bring the book to fruition.

This book is dedicated to Lynne, Christopher, Jonathan and Timothy, whose continual feedback and appraisal makes it all worthwhile.

CONTENTS

chapter 1

INTRODUCTION

'People have one thing in common. They are all different.'

Robert Zend

IN THE UNITED STATES OF AMERICA during the seventies and eighties, speed on the Interstate Highways was restricted to 55mph. Everywhere there were signs 'Stay Alive – Drive 55'. On long stretches, especially through remote areas, the traffic gradually sped up to around 70mph. This included the heavy goods vehicles that had radio networks keeping them well informed of the presence of State Troopers with their speed traps.

Suddenly, the traffic would slow down to the speed limit. In one or two miles the reason would become apparent. Sometimes it would be the Highway Patrol, parked on the central reservation between carriageways. On other occasions what seemed to be a patrol car turned out to be a life-size cardboard replica and this only became apparent at close range. Obviously, no one was going to be stopped for exceeding the speed limit by a piece of cardboard. However, its very presence had the desired effect of making drivers conscious of the limits and of staying within them.

Such it is with assessment. Any assessment process drives both learning and behaviour. It is a process of measuring progress against defined criteria, providing a snapshot of performance at a point in time usually for external consumption. It also keeps practice within bounds.

The drive towards the development of assessment and revalidation procedures within the United Kingdom has come from Government, anxious to recognise and deal with poor performance by medical staff. Similarly the profession itself would seek to ensure that the five or six percent of doctors who do underperform should be identified at an early stage with remedial action being taken as quickly as possible.

The potential danger of any system of assessment or revalidation is that it could become hierarchical and autocratic. If it is also centrally controlled, the loss of individual expression and the inability to adapt rapidly to local circumstances leads to demoralisation and demotivation of professional staff, the majority of whom deliver very high standards of care.

An appraisal system is slightly different in emphasis. It seeks to build on the *status quo* and assist staff in their professional development. It sets standards and objectives through the production of a Personal Development Plan, facilitates two-way feedback on performance, identifies training and development needs and then sets up a contract between management and staff for their achievement. The key to good clinical performance is not just to maintain but to increase motivation by properly utilising the feedback process. The ethos should be positive rather than negative, constructive rather than destructive and looking to the future rather than dwelling on the past. It therefore begins with an open dialogue about the present situation and then discusses and agrees the future direction.

These are hardly new concepts, having been developed, well tried and tested throughout industry. They have been shown to provide a sound basis for personal and corporate growth, team building and effective management at all levels.

Medical staff do not work in a vacuum but increasingly operate in teams that include doctors in other specialities, nurses, paramedics and other professionals as well as managers. This team concept is the foundation for clinical governance, which can be defined as 'corporate responsibility for clinical outcomes'. With any responsibility comes rights, and professional groupings have not just a right but an obligation to give and receive feedback, to and from individual members. Senior Clinicians continue to fulfil a leadership role, but it is now of a more democratic nature as opposed to the hierarchical dictatorship, however benign, that may have characterised relationships in the past.

Winning organisations must have clear strategic goals and operational objectives. Achieving these requires good systems to make sure everyone understands what is expected, and recognises their achievements by working in cooperation with them, providing regular feedback of a positive nature. They recognise and reward high achievers and help those further down the line to improve by offering appropriate mentoring and coaching so that they grow and develop towards the corporate goals of the organisation, hence for the ultimate benefit of the patients.

Change imposed is changed opposed. The implementation of an appraisal system is not an easy option since many believe it is a management tool to apportion blame and provide a basis for disciplinary action. If staff are not convinced of its value, then the appraisal system is doomed to failure. It is vital that all participants feel fully engaged in the development of the process and have a clear understanding of its function. In the UK, it has to be consistent with good medical practice as laid down by the General Medical Council and must link with clinical governance and revalidation procedures. However, it should not be perceived as punitive and should demonstrate an attitude of openness in the whole culture of the organisation. There must therefore be transparent objectivity in order to eliminate the destructive potential of personal bias. Such a culture will also present, at regular intervals, the opportunity for doctors to expose their concerns or disquiet about any factors within the health organisation that hinders their ability to deliver to the highest standards of patient care. Further, openness requires the provision of a relatively blame-free environment, where staff are encouraged to identify and tackle problems, such as critical incidents or near misses, without the constant threat of being subjected to disciplinary procedures.

The function of management is to improve the output of the organisation by achieving maximum benefit from its main resource, the staff. The workforce must be treated properly, as professionals, by involving them appropriately in the development of the service, providing necessary support and resources. This may include training and the facilities for supervision, counselling and mentoring as required.

This book recognises the potential tensions, ambivalence and the need for a step-by-step guide to the appraisal process. Drawing from the experience of industry, it provides a practical approach to the development of appraisal and ultimately assessment procedures within the Health Service. The model is generic so that it can be adapted to specific personnel and organisational needs. The object is to achieve a win-win situation by which the organisation benefits through improved clinical performance, and the staff benefit by allowing individuals to develop their own career ambitions. Appraisal must not be simply a form-filling exercise. It is a process not an event, and while the annual appraisal interview is a key milestone, the process is continuous.

Over a prolonged period, say three to five years, it should provide a clear and valid picture of how individuals perform in the full breadth of their professional life. This forms a more accurate basis for any revalidation of fitness to practice than a one-off assessment, however well constructed. If appraisal is approached half-heartedly, poorly implemented and is not fully understood or accepted by clinicians as being a practical exercise, it is doomed to failure. Further, it has to be recognised that those who appraise are themselves subject to appraisal. The managers are also the managed. This process has to be carried out correctly from the beginning and proper training is essential.

What follows is therefore a practical guide, written for all staff involved in the appraisal process from Chief Executive to the most junior trainee. It is rooted in practicality and the real world of medical practice, providing a step by step approach to the introduction of a successful Performance Appraisal System.

Individual clinicians will find themselves both in the role of appraiser and of appraisee and require an understanding of both roles. For the appraisee, chapters 6 and 7 will be the most pertinent to give an understanding of the process and the detail of their responsibilities. In addition, for those acting as appraisers, chapter 3 gives some background on motivating professionals and chapter 8 gives practical advice on dealing with difficult issues which may arise. For those managing the whole process, chapter 9 discusses how appraisal is integrated into operational management and chapter 10 gives a step-by-step guide for the successful introduction of an appraisal system to a unit or trust.

chapter 2
APPRAISAL, ASSESSMENT AND REVALIDATION

INTRODUCTION

SOME WITHIN THE medical profession would ask why it has suddenly become necessary to introduce systems of appraisal, assessment and revalidation in the Health Service. One factor is undoubtedly that, both nationally and internationally, there have been a few high profile cases which have attracted widespread media attention and have implied some doctors are not keeping up-to-date and called their clinical skills into question. However, although these cases have undoubtedly sparked the debate, the real issues are much wider and more complex than simply providing a mechanism to identify doctors who in some way are perceived to have underperformed.

Like it or not, times have changed for the medical profession. Gone are the days when senior staff could take up post and hope to practice with minimal change for the next 20 to 25 years until retirement. If one takes the amount of knowledge of clinical medicine generally available around 1950 and represent it by one unit, then by 1956 it had doubled. By 1962 it had doubled again. The pace then increased, doubling every four years and at present it is estimated that medical knowledge is advancing at such a rate that it is doubling every 18 months to two years. This exponential change is phenomenal, with the plethora of journals and now the internet ensuring rapid worldwide dissemination of potential advances in a very short time, sometimes without the benefit of appropriate peer review.

All doctors are now engaged in a process of lifelong learning and need to spend considerable time and energy keeping up with their speciality or subspeciality. This is both from a technical and a knowledge point of view, as well as being required to maintain a broad understanding of other developments within the profession so that they can work effectively in a team.

The rate of change requires that there should be some form of revalidation to ensure that professionals are keeping up-to-date. This is particularly necessary in medicine, where senior staff have a high degree of autonomy. They have considerable rights and privileges, but along with those must come responsibility and, very importantly, accountability for their actions. Revalidation exists to determine on a regular basis that doctors remain fit to practice in all aspects of their chosen field.

This chapter will look at the reasons for, and implications of, appraisal and assessment from the point of view of the individual clinician and management within the overall structure of the organisation. It will highlight the benefits for each in having a robust, structured process that is well understood and accepted by all parties. It will discuss how appraisal and assessment are fundamental components of any revalidation process.

WHAT CONSTITUTES APPRAISAL AND ASSESSMENT?

Appraisal and assessment are integral parts of any quality assurance programme. Superficially, it would seem that appraisal is for the benefit of the individual and assessment is something entirely different, being a method whereby the organisation and the public ensure that the individual or team is measured against some external standard. In fact, the reason for both is to ensure the delivery of a quality service to patients, one that reflects on what has been achieved as well as on the achievements of others in similar fields. Therefore, there is constant refreshment of practice, influenced by feedback from internal and external audit resulting in the maintenance of the highest standards in an ever-changing environment.

In medicine, appraisal and assessment deal with much more than purely clinical matters, but as well they broach interpersonal skills and ethical issues involving as they do feedback from as many sources as possible. Most importantly patients must be empowered to contribute. Appraisals are also about identifying likely risks to patients and taking immediate action before any serious problems develop. If a number of appraisals on an individual have been positive, showing appropriate growth and development, then they form the basis of an end point assessment or revalidation programme.

So what is the difference between appraisal and assessment? Both are used to drive learning and keep up performance, but they are fundamentally different in the way they operate. Both require the gathering of evidence of performance in a variety of areas and also demand a period of reflection. Appraisal is an ongoing dynamic process involving two-way communication by discussion and allowing for course corrections as circumstances change. It involves the three C's: cooperation, collaboration and compromise in order to inform, guide and develop an individual's potential, usually in line with the strategic objectives of the healthcare system. It should facilitate growth in other directions and, because of the two-way feedback, may well influence the setting of future directions by management. This is vital for the service to remain dynamic and keep abreast of professional trends. The emphasis is therefore on individual growth, development and performance and is basically for internal consumption.

Assessment has a different driving force. It can be seen as a snapshot in time, providing evidence for external consumption of levels of training and quality within the organisation. It is no longer two-way but involves judgement of the worth or value of a particular performance. It is used to make decisions based on the moment it is carried out. It is checked against external standards and is not usually subject to two-way feedback at the time, although it may be later through an appeals process. The three C's of appraisal are not much in evidence, but rather the fourth C of confrontation may be more obvious when things go wrong!

A revalidation system should be a mixture of both. There are many reasons why a single snapshot in time may not give a valid picture of overall performance. On the other hand some check of competence must be made to ensure quality standards are maintained. Revalidation should be based on multiple appraisals and assessments so that the end result does not contain any surprises. The combination of both appraisal and assessment starts a culture of setting objectives and standards as well as giving feedback of a positive nature to help growth. The whole intention is to identify any potential problems as early as possible, to identify training and development needs and to ensure these are carried out in order to provide a sound basis for revalidation.

ORGANISATIONAL CONTEXT

This process of appraisal and assessment for clinicians must be developed within the organisational context of the Health Service. Historically, the management structure in the Health Service has been flat, with ill-defined lines of accountability for consultants and permanent staff. The rapid advances in medical knowledge, coupled with the sheer complexity of the technology involved, have led to increasing specialisation requiring a team approach to the delivery of health care. Workloads have increased along with public expectations of what the Health Service can deliver and, inevitably, there has also been a rapid escalation in the costs involved.

From a clinical point of view, however well motivated the individual clinicians, these changes have given rise to considerable difficulty in guaranteeing the delivery of a high quality service which by definition keeps up with the latest advances, utilising the best results from evidence-based practice. This relates not only to the knowledge base, but also ensuring the development and maintenance of skills at the highest levels.

As an example, a surgeon in routine practice rarely has opportunity to operate with other fully-trained surgeons, and so has little chance for comparing skill levels. However, others in the operating room such as anaesthetists or theatre nurses may well be able to compare and contrast performance between a number of surgeons, making them a very important source of feedback.

The issue of calling to account has to be recognised as legitimate by everyone in public service. More than ever before, there is a need for a solid management structure throughout the organisation, and this has evolved over the last decade.

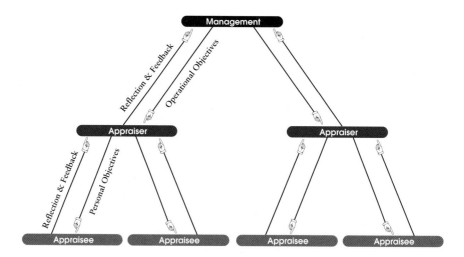

FIG. I INTERACTIVE FEEDBACK LOOPS IN THE MANAGEMENT SYSTEM

The role of management in the Health Service is to ensure that strategic and operational objectives are met by obtaining the best possible returns from the resources available, particularly the human resources. The two-way interaction involved in an appraisal process is therefore vital to the growth of the organisation. It is the main tool for implementing the strategic plan, setting standards and objectives, and providing feedback to the decision-makers. It has to identify training and development needs, with the end result being an agreement between management and the workforce in order to achieve the objectives.

From the point of view of clinicians the line management structure has developed as follows:

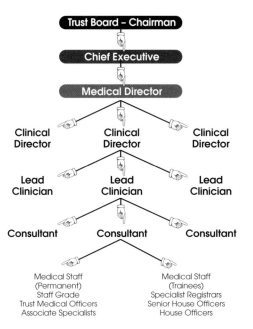

FIG.2 LINES OF ACCOUNTABILITY WITHIN A HEALTH SERVICE TRUST

All clinical staff have now been placed within the structure and corporate lines of accountability are clearly established. Staff appraisals are generally undertaken by those with line management responsibility. Since all are within the structure, it can be seen that those who carry out appraisals will themselves be subjected to the same process. For example, a lead clinician (who may for instance be a head of department) will appraise a number of other consultant staff, and in turn will be appraised by the medical director. This ensures two-way feedback at all levels.

The appraisal system should be empowering for both sides, since it is in the nature of a contract with rights and responsibilities allocated to both groups.

It must be consistent with good medical practice as laid down by regulatory bodies such as the General Medical Council. It must also be the link between clinical governance and any revalidation procedures. The objective is to ensure management, workforce, resources and training are channelled towards a common aim, in order to make the most efficient and effective use of each.

Accordingly, all within the structure must fully understand their roles both as an appraiser and an appraisee. They will therefore require appropriate training in these activities.

We will now look at the benefits of a properly instituted appraisal system as it relates on the one hand to individuals and on the other to those charged with the management and smooth running of the organisation.

BENEFITS OF AN APPRAISAL SYSTEM

INDIVIDUAL PERSPECTIVES

Even the suggestion of the introduction of an appraisal or assessment system can provoke fear, suspicion and cynicism amongst staff, leading at least to resistance and potentially refusal to fully participate or give the process more than lip service. Some may see the introduction of such a system as being an imposition and infringement of their rights, because they feel it is going to be imposed as a management tool for disciplinary purposes. They do not regard it as being something developed in collaboration with them and see no positive benefits either to their patients or, it must be said, to themselves.

The purpose of the exercise is to improve the organisation's performance, specifically by enhancing the performance of individuals, and this needs to be communicated in a positive way. A process is needed which avoids anger and unnecessary confrontation, as this leads to low morale and demotivation. The intention is to guide individuals in a particular direction in keeping with Health Service targets. If this is done badly it creates tension within a hospital, leading to bad relationships between peers and management, and can result in undue importance being given to frivolous issues.

Well motivated staff with high morale is essential for any organisation to move forward. Motivation and professionalism must pervade the management structure.

The importance of morale and motivation was shown by a study undertaken by Elton Mayo 70 years ago at the Western Electric Factory in Chicago. His experiments matched a study group with controls in the same factory with similar production lines. Both the experimental groups and the control groups were informed that they were participating in a study.

To begin with, better lighting was given to the experimental group and over the study period output rose in both study and control groupings. This was followed by other alterations in working practice such as more worker friendly hours and longer breaks. Again, production increased in both groupings. The most startling finding was that when all alterations in work practice were restored to the previously accepted norms, output soared yet again. Mayo's conclusion was that job satisfaction and therefore output increased not just because of extra perks, but also because workers felt they were being valued and that their opinions mattered.

19

Appraisal will work best if it is seen to involve sharing and solving as opposed to calling to account. A motivated workforce is characterised by a drive to develop, helping each other to move forward in a system which rewards progress and achievement fairly and consistently. Nevertheless, appraisal must be capable of identifying and supporting individuals when level of performance seems to be an issue.

This is achieved in the first instance by the production of an agreed personal development plan, usually on an annual basis, which creates focus and clearly targets the expectations of the staff, letting them know where they are going and what is expected of them. These objectives are written down and provide boundaries as well as defining expectations. The personal development plan also contains a commitment from management which may be in terms of finance, appropriate equipment, a good working environment with adequate support staff, or the provision of training as necessary. In other words, management agrees (in what is in fact a contract) to commit appropriate resources.

The appraisal interview is structured in order to highlight achievement and to acknowledge when expectations have been exceeded. It is a review against levels of job performance and outcomes which have been previously agreed. Any lack of performance should also become obvious, but the nature of the two-way discussion and feedback allows full exploration of the reasons why such deficiencies have occurred and whether or not the cause was external to the appraisee. Professionals therefore have the opportunity to feed back to management any constraint and limitation on their performance, due for instance to lack of equipment or staff which should be considered to be management issues. There is also the opportunity to highlight problems which may be arising in other areas or support departments such as a laboratory.

Setting such targets and having them agreed in writing in advance is a very powerful form of protection for the professional from undue criticism. It replaces innuendo with a process that can be seen to be both open and fair, providing an equitable situation which can be demonstrated externally. There is better communication at all levels giving an early warning of problems or indeed grievances.

If properly run, the process should result in staff being able to form an objective view of their own performance since it can be very difficult for individuals to assess themselves in an everyday work environment. Senior clinicians rarely have the opportunity to observe or work with others of their peer group. It is very difficult to obtain good feedback about competency although it is much better to receive this on an ongoing basis rather than find out after 15 or 20 years that the performance was not regarded as satisfactory, especially if this ends up as the subject of a disciplinary tribunal or action in the civil courts.

When first introduced the appraisal system may appear somewhat threatening to established clinicians, but once it has been in position for several years it no longer constitutes a threat. Junior staff brought up in such a system will come to welcome feedback. They listen and learn by asking for specific examples and evidence from the experience of others. If there is criticism, they quickly learn to accept it if the reasons are clearly given and they can then move forward with confidence on the basis of the help they have received. A proper system replaces subjective criticism which can be biased, facilitating an objective critique against targets and standards, which have been previously jointly agreed and committed to paper.

Appraisal also presents the opportunity to discuss career development on a regular basis. Aspirations can be brought out in the open and fully discussed in the light of the strategic objectives of the organisation. Opportunities for advancement may emerge when operational management takes into account the strengths of the various components of the workforce in order to try and achieve the strategic objectives. There is room for negotiation, for instance by agreeing to take on some extra responsibility individuals may obtain commitment from management towards their own development and training needs. They are in a process of mutual problem solving.

In the past it has often been difficult for people to speak positively about themselves in an interview situation. This has been taken as a sign of arrogance. The focus has therefore inevitably been on deficiencies and consequently it can be difficult to generate the drive and motivation to make positive changes. Confidence comes from feedback that acknowledges successes and achievements. It is not a sign of arrogance if confidence is based on fact, and, when properly harnessed, such self-belief can drive an individual to even greater heights. Finally, there is the opportunity for clinicians to feedback both at an operational and strategic level, using their experience and professionalism to influence future developments. This sense of ownership can be the greatest motivator of all leading to increased job satisfaction and a sense of personal value.

21

MANAGEMENT PERSPECTIVE
Almost 100 years ago Henry Ford said:

'The problem is that each time I hire a pair of hands, I also get a person'.

Hierarchical and autocratic forms of management tend to use appraisal and assessment as a threat. The emphasis in the past has been on how to control and discipline the workforce. This simply does not work when an organisation is dependent on skill, knowledge and particularly on the judgement of individuals to adapt on a daily basis to changes on the ground. Organisations do not deliver healthcare, individual professionals do and it is their judgement from minute to minute and day-to-day that influences the quality of what is delivered.

Over 100 years after Henry Ford, the underlying premise of management is now:

'Each time I hire a pair of hands, I also get a brain'.

The Health Service itself is growing and developing and the pace of change is exponential. As with any company, the organisation has three main aims namely: volume, quality and cost. It has to ensure a volume of throughput, done efficiently and effectively, keeping control of cost, and at the same time providing a quality service. A motivated workforce moving forward in an agreed direction best serves such quality. It is hindered when employees are demotivated by insensitive hierarchical edicts giving them a feeling of alienation. The appraisal and assessment system is the backbone of the quality assurance programme. The purpose is to ensure that everyone from the Chief Executive to the intern is on board and that management, workforce, resources and training are all closely aligned.

It is fundamental that the organisation has a clear corporate vision, usually translated into a three to five year rolling strategic plan that must be understood at all levels within the organisation. Without this, to quote Mager: 'If you do not know where you are going, it is very difficult to know how to get there - and also to know when you have arrived.'

The strategic plan must be translated into a business plan and then an operational level plan for each department with specific targets and outcomes. If this is not carried out in sufficient detail, there is an expectation gap between those who decide and those who do. This gap needs to be bridged in as seamless a fashion as possible. A proper appraisal system promotes and rewards a culture within its workforce that values the efficiency and quality in the service delivered to patients. It therefore is a powerful method for harnessing the internal motivation for the workforce, guiding it gently towards the operational and strategic objectives and allowing professionals' undoubted ability to flourish, thereby driving up overall standards.

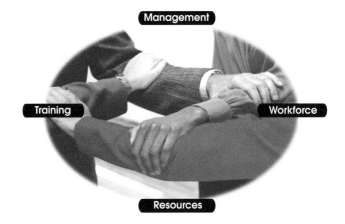

FIG.3 ALIGNING THE ORGANISATION

Feedback from the workforce to the top levels of the organisation allows a trust board and its management team to plan ahead for new contracts and developments, and to identify any training that is required. The more effective an organisation is at communicating its objectives and values and of receiving feedback, then the better the performance is likely to be due to an increased sense of cohesiveness and loyalty within the ranks giving rise to high morale and strong motivation. This allows the development of a culture of continuous improvement and success, i.e. lifelong learning at all levels, which keeps the organisation vibrant and alive with a high morale which comes from a feeling of success.

At an operational level, the business of healthcare delivery is extremely complex, and even within a particular branch such as surgery, there are multiple sub-specialities. Nowadays, it is virtually impossible for clinical directors to know the detail of a colleague's job, particularly if they are not in exactly the same speciality. A line manager may find himself appraising someone who may clinically have greater experience and expertise. This must be recognised and any hierarchy that develops needs to be democratic and evolutionary. Indeed, the appraisal system requires the input of the professional workforce. Their feedback on the delivery and quality of services provided to patients is extremely important for the image and development of the organisation. The key is to obtain cooperation and not manage by compulsion.

At the same time, staff do require guidance on the standards of good practice which underpin healthcare policy. It has to be acknowledged that a certain percentage of individuals 'underperform' when compared to their peers. Indeed, in any large group, the levels of performance will follow a normal distribution. Inevitably in all organisations, some individuals will not achieve the desired objectives and outputs, and through the appraisal process the reasons should be explored and resolved. This may be due to a number of factors, such as lack of knowledge or skill on the part of the individual, and can be corrected by the provision of appropriate training, coaching and mentoring. On the other hand the problem may be with the allocation of resources and again management has its part to play.

However, if it turns out that the underperformance is due to an attitudinal problem in that the individual is competent and can perform if he wished to, then this also becomes very obvious. Many factors may be involved, for instance interpersonal relationships at work or other personal problems such as worries over finance, health or within partnerships at home. Any organisation that values its personnel will try to handle these as sensitively as possible since any lack of performance may be temporary. Alternatively, if the lack of performance is by choice, then it must be confronted and challenged. Hopefully the mere fact that it is directly challenged will have the desired effect of correction but if not, then unfortunately it becomes a disciplinary issue. This is a totally different process and, although the necessity for it may be identified during the appraisal process, the disciplinary procedure must be seen as a separate entity.

It becomes apparent that the interaction between the appraiser and the appraisee can be a very powerful relationship builder. If, on the other hand, the relationship breaks down, there are potentially serious consequences for

23

the working of any unit. Training is essential at all levels and it is important that all staff should be governed by the same process so that there is transparency and fairness and the staff build up a confidence in the system.

Both the individual and the manager base the personal development plan on the production of clearly documented objectives. These give a proper sense of direction with signposts along the way for monitoring progress. One of the basic principles of adult education is the use of signposts. A practitioner needs time to reflect, to put the experience into context and to gauge whether appropriate goals and objectives are being achieved. It is this reflection on practice that forms the backbone of any quality assurance programme. If performance turns out to be below expectation, then account is taken of any change in circumstances to give a balanced review. It is about recognising abilities and potential, helping people to develop their knowledge, skills and attitude.

Management therefore needs to develop an overview of both the individual and of complete departments, identifying, in consultation with them, ideas for movement towards the strategic objectives. The strategic plan must be kept in focus and feedback loops are essential for an organisation to succeed. The corporate vision must be accepted by the workforce and indeed can only be implemented by them. By encouraging and motivating them, their enthusiasm and drive become infectious, highlighting new issues and trends so that they can be taken on board and contribute to the planning process. The more dynamic the feedback loops the more successful the organisation will be at adapting as it grows.

One of the positive benefits of a clear appraisal system is that areas of concern can be identified fairly quickly before there are consequences that damage the reputation of the organisation. This will only occur in an open, supportive environment. In a punitive system, people are inclined to hide problems until they become so obvious that they simply burst through their protective wall and create havoc. A system that respects its workforce but yet has very clear guidelines of behavioural standards which are transparent, moral and at the same time are seen to be fair, is most likely to result in identifying those who, for one reason or another, are underperforming at a particular time. They can be helped to come to terms with the problem, assisted in their development by retraining or redeployment or enabled to make other creative decisions before there are unacceptable outcomes for patient care.

An important benefit of appraisal and assessment from the management point of view is the agreement of action plans and deadlines. This extrinsic drive encourages people to finish the tasks they have agreed. This is vital if different people or departments are required to complete tasks in a particular sequence, because if one person does not finish their portion in time then others cannot complete or, in some cases, even start the next stage.

Both appraisal and assessment drive learning and behavioural change. The bottom line is that by working with its resources, most management, especially human resources is aiming to ensure the safe and effective functioning of the unit and delivery of healthcare. Appraisal is the basic tool. **25**

Finally, any organisation needs good managers. Although concentrating heavily on clinical matters, one important spin-off from the interaction is the potential to identify personnel with good management skills. Given appropriate training, some individuals may welcome the opportunity for a partial or complete change of career direction, and assume greater management responsibilities.

CONCLUSION

Service delivery is a partnership between those who manage and those who are directly responsible for patient care. It is a team effort requiring clear goals with robust feedback mechanisms ensuring that those goals are achieved. Appraisal is the cement that binds management and workforce into a professional unit for the delivery of efficient, effective and quality healthcare. It binds the whole organisation, with the feedback system helping planners to formulate a strategic plan taking full account of advice from the professional workforce.

Management at all levels obtains an overview of individual job plans and complete departments that will indicate areas of improvement and growth. This allows objectives to be stated at both a team and individual level, and be aligned with those of departments in the organisation as a whole. Management can reprioritise targets based on the feedback from professionals, and can use this to increase job satisfaction forming as productive a relationship with the workforce as possible.

For the appraisee, there is a clear understanding of what is expected and agreement that they will be involved in negotiations on how those expectations are to be achieved. It allows mutual problem solving for issues arising in the workplace, and if these can be dealt with before a crisis arises then this can maintain and improve working relationships.

Overall, people work best when they have a positive self-image and view of their capabilities. A good appraisal system should emphasise that. How individuals respond to being appraised reflects their feelings about themselves. If they feel well treated, they are motivated to move forward. If they are constantly criticised they become defensive and it is very difficult to motivate them to change direction. At the end of the day, a good appraisal system will lead to a confident, competent and well motivated medical staff.

26 The rapid advances in medicine do mean that there can be radical changes in the knowledge and skill base over relatively short periods of time. Assessment and revalidation are therefore very much live issues. They must be based on the totality of job performance over time and therefore a single snapshot assessment would be far too simplistic and totally inappropriate. The ongoing appraisal system coupled with other indicators of performance such as clinical audit, participation in continuing medical educational activities and feedback from patients and peers, will provide the most solid platform for any revalidation procedure.

chapter 3
MOTIVATING PROFESSIONALS

INTRODUCTION

MANAGEMENT IS THE SCIENCE of organising and motivating people to produce a desired outcome. It is about influencing behaviour so that there is a will to act in line with the needs of the organisation. People are individualistic, and at any one time different individuals will have different priorities. These priorities are not static and may well change over time. A knowledge of motivation is vital to those managing the system, not just in the positive sense of understanding what motivates people but, perhaps more importantly, understanding what is likely to demotivate. By definition, motivation requires a change from the *status quo*. It is not that people resist change, but rather that they resist others changing them!

This chapter explores two main theories of motivation that come closest to helping us understand how best to encourage the optimum performance from professionals. It will look at the impact of personal orientation and using the two together, will discuss ways of enthusing and supporting those who are responsible for the delivery of the service.

MOTIVATION THEORIES

MASLOW

The most basic levels are the physiological and security needs with the theory being, that if these are not satisfied then an individual is driven towards seeking them. Once they are satisfied, an individual tends to move up to the next level with the top being self-actualisation, realising individual potential, winning and achieving. However, if having moved up the ladder, a lower level becomes significantly disturbed for example by problems at home, then the tendency is to switch attention to try and re-secure that lower level.

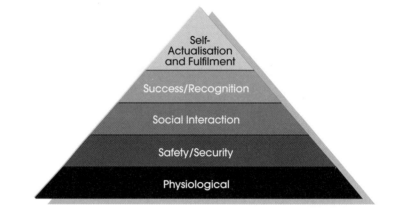

FIG. I MASLOW'S HIERARCHY OF NEEDS

Professionals tend to function at the higher levels. Usually, they have relative financial security and if they also have a secure home base, they move on to the higher levels of seeking recognition, praise and the opportunity to succeed and to feel successful. Most professionals are motivated by their own concept of success. Success is not simply achieving a goal, but rather the 'emotion of motion' towards various objectives which they inherently value. The feeling of movement in the desired direction and the gratification it brings helps build a positive self-image. External recognition enhances self-esteem, so the drive towards achievement is built around obtaining growth and self-actualisation from tasks. This is usually enhanced by being given increased responsibility, thus enriching the job and making it more prestigious and satisfying.

Professional staff like to be kept 'in the picture', and to be briefed about what is happening. They need the opportunity to meet and discuss issues with other professionals and managers and will resist simply being told what to do. Good information flow is essential between them, their peer group and management. They will commit themselves more strongly to targets they have suggested or helped to develop. Professionals must therefore be part of the process that sets their objectives.

Conversely, demotivation can all too easily be brought about by a lack of delegated responsibility, by failure to engage in objective and target setting and by an absence of information and feedback. Most professionals resent an authoritarian style of management especially if it lacks or appears to lack clear direction and if they feel they are being ignored, demeaned, excluded and then blamed when things go wrong. They value freedom and must be given opportunities and support to try new ideas and skills as long as they are within acceptable and agreed bounds.

HERZBERG

Herzberg's theories were based on what he termed motivators and hygiene factors. Hygiene factors are basic needs that do not of themselves motivate, but if they are not present they demotivate leading to marked dissatisfaction. They can range from the most seemingly trivial such as a dedicated parking space or assume considerable importance, for instance in being able to choose the time of a holiday. Job security is important with insecurity undermining motivation at all levels. Finance also comes under the heading of hygiene factors. A good basic level of pay is important along with bonuses, especially if there is a high financial outlay such as a young family and a mortgage. However, at a later stage if finance is not so pressing, for instance when the mortgage and other debts have been paid off, then the drive to work hard with associated stresses is likely to diminish.

29

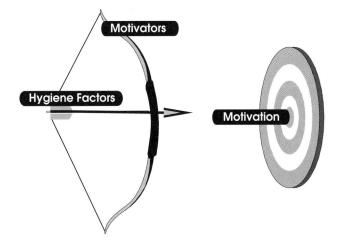

FIG.2 HERZBERG'S MOTIVATION THEORY

Motivators on the other hand drive people to achieve. They are built around obtaining growth and self-actualisation including having the appropriate resources available to carry out the job in hand. Achievement and recognition enhance self-esteem and professionals prefer jobs that are positive and personally satisfying. They seek a degree of autonomy and a feeling of control over their day to day life. They like to be kept up-to-date with developments, to be treated fairly and with an appropriate recognition of their position. They value meeting and discussing issues with other professionals and management whom they also expect to be professionally competent. They do not respond well to being told what to do and require that information flows in both directions.

It is therefore clear that individual circumstances may dictate hygiene factors and motivators and those undoubtedly vary over time. Money is a motivator at a low level, but the main power motivators are recognition, praise and the opportunity to succeed.

PERSONAL ORIENTATION

People have three basic orientations: towards others, towards task or towards self. Some professionals require social interaction and relate best as part of a group, frequently where they feel that they have some leadership or control. If they do not have that interaction and feedback, they quickly become demotivated. Others are very much task focused. They may well like working in a group but their prime concern is the achievement of the task in hand and that is what drives them. Sometimes a hobby and work can be the same thing and task-orientated individuals often become workaholics with work coming first at all times. It is important to them that their work is done to a high standard. They are best motivated when they see the importance of their task and its overall relevance. They require constant reassurance and praise. Those whose orientation is towards self have a high degree of self-awareness and are interested in learning and striving to improve their performance. Again, they need to have objectives which stretch them and are fulfilled by achieving those goals. While they do respond to praise, they are generally much more self-sufficient than those who are task related.

It is important when considering how best to motivate each individual, to take into account whether their orientation is predominantly towards people, task or self-fulfilment. Look at their activities and try to determine whether they are very sociable, do they like working in groups, do they focus very clearly on tasks perhaps even to the exclusion of others, or do they spend a lot of time advancing themselves, for example by reading or taking extra courses.

The reaction to a given situation will depend on the orientation that is in the ascendancy for that individual. For instance, someone who is more people than task orientated will tend to put family concerns above career advancement if there is an element of choice. Therefore, if offered a prospect of promotion requiring longer hours or a move, they may refuse it if the consequences would be a significant disruption of their family life. On the other hand, another individual who is more task than people orientated may well take the opportunity for advancement. Neither is right or wrong, it simply depends on their view point.

MOTIVATION IN THE WORK PLACE

It becomes apparent from the above that in order to motivate it is important to determine orientation and to think of all those factors both at home and at work which may influence behaviour. Someone young or new to the workforce may need to be frequently recognised for their skills. They are generally keen to have a good level of pay and an interesting job with a chance of promotion, but may also be coping with the demands of a young family and may well need time off for personal life. More experienced staff need security of tenure, possibly some form of bonus, and may also require status in the organisation and to have delegated responsibility for key tasks. Their initiative must be encouraged and this requires them to be given empowerment in an environment that recognises their contribution. Senior staff should be asked for their ideas and these should be implemented as far as reasonable. If ideas are rejected then reasons should be given. It is most important that professionals and their teams have a clear idea of the strategic direction and the operational objectives. They must then be given latitude to plan how the objective should be achieved. They must have scope to vary the method, sequence and pace of work, coupled with control information to monitor their own performance. In other words, a dictatorship of objectives but a democracy of means.

Clinical freedom is a healthy and appropriate concept, allowing growth and development but within certain limits. This is rather similar to sporting activities such as a football match. There are boundaries to the pitch and clear rules of the game. However within these an individual can choose a position and decide to be a forward, a back or a goal keeper. During the game he can choose to run with the ball or pass it, but in each case with the clear objective of getting the ball into the opponent's net. He cannot, however, change the rules. He also cannot break the rules without penalties. If he commits a foul, he will get a clear warning and if he does it again he may be sent off. If he does not wish to follow the rules or obey the referee, then he cannot play the game.

In clinical practice, there is the same concept of freedom within bounds. If clinicians start to work as autocrats, ignoring the boundaries created by the legal, moral and ethical rules of society and of the profession, then problems occur. However, if the boundaries are set sensibly and reviewed in the light of advances then they need not be seen as restrictive and so allow for the professional entrepreneur who is vital to progress. Initiative requires empowerment.

Senior medical staff are required to do much more than clinical work. At any one time they also are teachers, researchers and managers. These are of themselves vast fields of endeavour and are continually developing. Therefore, continuing education in these matters is required. Generally, consultants are high achievers and become dissatisfied when they are not confident in all aspects of their job. Loss of face is an important consideration for them. They are driven to learn and feel better when they have both practical experience and knowledge. Therefore, training of itself can be motivating.

The process of achievement is at least as important as the attainment of targets and success cannot simply be defined in terms of outputs and numbers. Clinical departments are a very complex environment and patient outcomes are achieved as a result of team effort. Individuals have to be part of teams but need recognition for their unique contribution by being noticed and appreciated. Having the ability to share ideas and encourage others to participate in putting together plans is a very powerful motivator as people commit themselves more strongly to targets they have helped to develop, agree and implement. There should also be a reward for team efforts. A simple example would be when the department achieves the required savings and then is given a financial reward, perhaps to develop another project. This represents a tangible benefit for their cooperation.

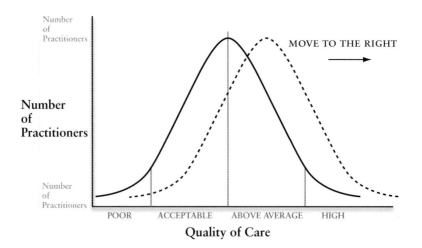

FIG.3 LEVELS OF PERFORMANCE

Any appraisal system must be designed to encourage growth. In any large working group, levels of performance will follow a bell shaped curve or normal distribution.

The role of management is to shift the curve to the right, indicating an increase in the quality of practice and hence the quality of care. A standard is, by definition, the lowest level of acceptable performance. It would be quite impossible to make the performance of all equal to the best, but by repeatedly encouraging and supporting continuous improvement the curve will shift to the right leaving fewer in, or even eliminating all together, the 'underperforming' tail.

33

Increase in performance depends not only on the competency but also the attitude of the staff. A system whose main concern is damage limitation by subjecting the whole body to rigorous and stifling controls coupled with intrusive monitoring of standards may well identify the bottom five per cent who underperform, but can also be so demoralising to the rest of the work force that they lose interest. This demotivation will have the consequence of either keeping the curve static or shifting it to the left. This would be a disaster for any enterprise, since organisations, like all living things, must grow to survive. Feedback is vital to motivation, positive feedback encourages whereas negative criticism and dispute has a disproportionately greater effect in the opposite direction. This can easily destroy not only individuals but teams, and ultimately the organisation itself.

INTRINSIC AND EXTRINSIC MOTIVATION

The most powerful driving force is intrinsic motivation. People will achieve more consistently over time when they enjoy and are motivated by what they do. All too often, instead of the carrot something more akin to a stick is used by way of attempts at external motivation. Undoubtedly, this can work well in the short term and people can be forced along a particular path either to gain a specific incentive or to avoid an unpleasant consequence. Not all extrinsic motivation is bad and it can be a powerful reinforcement of internal motivation, for instance in achieving a deadline for a particular task. The most classic example is examinations. If the topic to be examined is one that is useful to and enjoyed by an individual, then what is learned may well have a very positive long-term benefit. However, if the examination is of a subject in which the individual has little interest, then cramming that results in only short-term retention may be used simply to pass the examination. Often the information is forgotten within a matter of weeks. The effective combination of extrinsic motivation reinforcing intrinsic motivation is the most powerful for long-term achievement and effective team building.

CONCLUSION

Motivation of the work force is key to the success of any organisation. While motivation and morale are not the same thing, they are heavily linked. A well motivated group is likely to have a positive influence not only on their own morale but also on those around them particularly when there is a sense of achievement.

34 Perceptions and feelings are all important. Most professionals need a sense of security and consistency in the work place and they require feedback giving recognition of their achievements as they grow and develop. Status, being the degree of responsibility and control over the work environment, is important to self-esteem. Constant change over which they have no control is virtually guaranteed to demotivate even the most self-sufficient individuals, and undermines a dynamic and successful organisation.

An appraisal system works best when it guides and motivates staff towards strategic objectives. It tests whether the management, work force, resources and training strategy have all aimed in a common direction and should not be restrictive. It must consider the needs of the individual and, using motivational theory, seek to encourage self-development and active participation both as an individual and in a group setting, towards common goals.

Interviews that are carried out simply because they are mandated and consist of sitting at a desk, asking standard questions in order to tick boxes provided by the personnel department and resulting in half an hour or more of criticism given 'as feedback for your own good' is a sure way to destroy morale and create friction.

More generally, those in a leadership position need to be continually aware of morale within their teams. Steps should be taken to gauge this by seeking opinions on various important issues. This may be done through informal discussions, through team meetings, departmental meetings and through surveys and comments/suggestions boxes. Signs of dropping morale can include lack of cooperation, explicit obstructiveness or backbiting and blaming others for shortcomings. There may also be poor timekeeping, absenteeism or a decrease in either quantity or quality of treatment given to patients.

Focus groups may be useful for exploring significant concerns or difficulties. When the team agrees solutions, they must be acted upon. Management must be fully committed to the process and the outcomes since high performance may also demand additional organisational resources. No one can be autonomous and there must be a synergy between the objectives of the organisation and those of the senior staff. In order to give their best, professionals need to feel part of the decision making process and hence have ownership of the objectives.

chapter 4
THE NATURE
OF ASSESSMENT

INTRODUCTION

WHILST THERE ARE many different types of assessment, the four most relevant to the issues of Appraisal and Assessment in the Health Service are:

Criterion-Based

Norm-Based

Self-Based

Limen-Based

Each group is characterised by the nature of the standards applied, and in this chapter their potential relevance to assessing professionals is reviewed.

The nature of evidence collected, written, observational or through discussion, is also considered, along with the types of analysis of the results.

Each type of assessment will be reviewed at in the light of its purpose, whether it is to simply label personnel or to support and guide individuals in their learning as it relates to personal and clinical development. It is vital that each type of assessment is rigorously tested against the conditions of acceptability namely validity, reliability, feasibility and fidelity. This chapter therefore begins by defining these concepts then considers the effects of assessment before discussing the four main types of assessment.

CONDITIONS OF ACCEPTABILITY

VALIDITY

There are a number of classifications of validity but underlying them all is the concept that a particular method must measure what it is supposed to measure. For example, as a measure of intelligence, one could decide to record circumference of the head with a concept that the greater the circumference, the larger the brain and therefore the more intelligence. Superficially it may sound reasonable but manifestly it is not. On the other hand, serial recordings of head circumference in the first few weeks of life may give a valid indication of the development of hydrocephalus.

38 RELIABILITY

This implies that a method of assessment will come up with the same result no matter how often it is recorded providing the object of the measurement is static. It should also be free of observer or equipment error therefore different doctors using different tape measures should be able to measure the circumference of the head and come up with the same result.

FEASIBILITY

In order to check whether a surgeon is competent in the all round management of a particular procedure, it may be reasonable to suggest that observations are carried out by a number of people looking at and questioning all interventions for twenty or thirty similar procedures. This may be a valid and reliable method of checking competence but it is unlikely anyone could put in the manpower and resources to carry it out except in very specific instances.

FIDELITY

Fidelity implies what is happening in the real world and whether a method of measurement gives a good indication of what occurs in practice. The fact that someone can describe the steps of an operation and demonstrate some skills on a simulator, does not necessarily imply that they are competent to carry out actual operative procedures.

It is virtually impossible to find a measure which at the same time is fully valid, highly reliable, feasible and reflects real practice. In any compromise situation, validity must be the number one consideration. If not, we fall foul of McNamara's Fallacy: to make what is measurable important as opposed to what is important measurable. In terms of revalidation of medical practitioners, it has been suggested that a multiple-choice question paper would be an appropriate method. This may be quite feasible in that it would be easy to administer and mark, and extending it to matching choice questions may give some evidence of decision making, i.e. fidelity for clinical practice. It may give reliable results but it is most certainly not valid. Clinical practice involves more than pure medical knowledge and the ability to answer a multiple-choice question paper does not mean that a surgeon is capable of carrying out a Laparoscopic Cholecystectomy or a Cardiologist of inserting a pacemaker. Nor does it give any indication as regards ethical values or interpersonal relationships, all of which are extremely important for a practising clinician.

A range of techniques is therefore required from a range of observers. Whatever method is used must reflect the real world but it is not feasible to check every area of practice in depth. Therefore, sampling of some sort will have to occur and the selection of the sample can itself introduce bias.

COLLECTION OF DATA

Written methods would appear to save time for the assessor and allow a number of assessments to be carried out together. The questions may be standard. However, there is a lack of flexibility and the answers obtained only reflect the questions asked. Considerable time may therefore be required in formulating the precise questions, reading and interpreting the results. An easily marked multiple-choice question paper is at a very low level on the hierarchy of learning whereas most of the important information in professional practice is at the higher levels required for clinical judgement. Essay type questions that allow more freedom of thought are much more difficult and time consuming to mark and the objectivity which is a strength of the multiple-choice technique is lost. Decision-making can be very individual and therefore subject to bias on both sides.

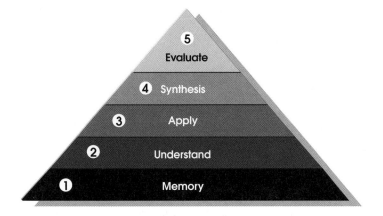

FIG.1 THE HIERARCHY OF LEARNING

Observation may be carried out in the workplace or in a simulated environment. Certain standards may be laid down, but if these are tightly controlled, they allow very little adaptation to the real situation since in practice the textbook patient or textbook operation rarely exists. It is unlikely that a textbook response would be appropriate without some discussion. In order to make such a method reliable, it requires multiple observers watching multiple situations and would not be feasible on a large scale in terms of cost and resources. It may however be achievable if a small cohort of people who appear to be consistently underperforming can be clearly identified.

Discussion methods allow much more freedom of movement over a range of topics. However they are very open to bias not just in the nature of the topics under discussion but also personal biases between the participants.

EFFECTS OF ASSESSMENT

BIAS

Every action has a reaction, sometimes positive and sometimes negative. The problem is that whether a reaction is deemed to be positive or negative is a subjective decision on behalf of the person undertaking the measurement. Most people feel very comfortable with change, as long as it is happening to someone else! We all have our in-built ideas based on past experience which provide the criteria against which we judge the world around us. Therefore, if individuals base their judgement against different internal criteria, they may easily come to different conclusions. In other words, they display prejudice. To try and overcome the likelihood of this occurring, the criteria need to be agreed in advance and to be as objective as possible. Unfortunately, this can also lead to inflexibility when either people or the situation demands movement. In matters of clinical judgement when there is unlikely to be one right answer for any given situation, this becomes extremely important.

HALO EFFECT AND RECENCY

Both of these relate to observer bias. The Halo Effect implies the observer is affected by previous information. For instance, to be told that an individual being assessed is an eminent Professor and expert in his field, is likely to colour any subjective impression gained by the observer especially if the period under review is short term. It represents a lack of objectivity in a critical analysis. This may also be seen in terms of research findings, where papers from a well-known institution may be received more favourably than an equally robust paper perhaps expressing a different view from a different hospital or university.

Recency is slightly different and implies the observer has some knowledge of the person being assessed. A bias in the interpretation of assessments may occur for better or worse depending on whether the recent experience was felt to be positive or negative. Giving someone the benefit of the doubt based on how they have performed in the past is an obvious example.

THE HEISENBERG EFFECT

Something that is being measured is liable to alter simply due to it being measured or more particularly due to the influence of specific techniques. A simple example would be an attempt to measure the temperature of a cup of tea by inserting a thermometer. If the thermometer is at a different temperature to the tea, there will be an equalising adjustment and the temperature actually recorded will not be the initial temperature of the tea. Particular techniques could have the same effect, for instance using a video to record a clinical interview may alter the behaviour of the clinician or the patient. The mere fact that an appraisal and assessment interview is scheduled may alter behaviour especially in those areas which are listed for discussion with the result that a true picture is not achieved. This may not matter and indeed, like most deadlines such as with examinations, may ensure that tasks that have been put on a back burner for a while are completed.

COMPETITION

Within most individuals or teams, there is some element of competitiveness. They may not strive to be the absolute best but few revel in being the worst when assessed against other groupings. Indeed most have a problem with being called average and yet by definition, roughly 50% must be average or below and attempts by those in the lower grades to become 'above average' have the effect of raising the average mark, still leaving approximately 50% average or below. Obviously this can be utilised to drive up standards but it is a very crude method of doing so in the long-term since, again, it may not take into account individual circumstances, for instance types of patients dealt with or the resources available.

PERCEIVED IMPORTANCE

It is very important that both the assessors and those being assessed attach a degree of importance to the outcome and the ongoing nature of the process. For instance, in terms of appraisal, if decisions are made and not adhered to, if promises are made and not kept, then the whole exercise becomes futile, falls into disrepute and loses all credibility.

It is also of great importance to decide to whom any results or conclusions will be communicated, how public they will be and what will be the likely consequence of a failure to perform. If those being appraised or assessed understand that punitive measures are liable to be undertaken against them, they are unlikely to admit any shortcomings. If, on the other hand, they perceive that problems will be fairly addressed in a non-threatening way and to their benefit, they are much more likely to open up and discuss potentially troublesome issues. Again, it is the perception of what is likely to happen that counts.

42 BUREAUCRACY

Any assessment process requires one or more people to manage it. There is therefore the possibility, if they are not themselves subjected to the same process, they assume the 'mantle of righteousness' and a hierarchical structure starts to develop. Whilst this may be acceptable in some situations and particularly when overseeing those in training, it can be counterproductive in a peer group setting. The problem is kept to a minimum if the standards under discussion are as objective as possible, particularly if they are nationally agreed.

TYPES OF ASSESSMENT

CRITERION-BASED

Most have undergone such a type of assessment for instance a driving test. A number of objective standards are set and those being assessed either do or do not achieve them.

	Satisfactory	Not Satisfactory
MCQ 30/35		
Read Number Plate at 10 Meters		
Checked Mirror		
Three Point Turn		
Emergency Stop		
Etc		
Pass	**Yes**	**No**

FIG.2 CRITERION-BASED ASSESSMENT FOR A DRIVING TEST

This type of assessment deals with standards that are, as previously discussed, the lowest acceptable level of performance. Therefore, the measurement is of low levels of behaviour in terms of knowledge, skills or attitude. It gives a base line but is not appropriate when attempting to achieve excellence. Further, it becomes a broad-brush approach if it is used to assess a large number of people. At a professional level, people tend to have areas of special interest where they may have more expertise than others. If an assessment is broad ranging, it may be to their detriment. An example would be to set one hundred multiple-choice questions to assess the knowledge base of surgeons. In order to be fair, it would have to cover all aspects of surgery including general, neuro, orthopaedic, ENT, etc. It might be quite difficult for someone specialised in arthroscopic surgery to pass such a test yet they may be extremely experienced and competent at what they do. On the other hand, a junior surgeon, recently qualified, may have no problem in answering the questions. Accordingly, in order to assess specialist surgeons, numerous multiple-choice question papers would have to be produced, perhaps dealing with each speciality but even within orthopaedic surgery there are now a number of specialisms. Would it be reasonable to downgrade an arthroscopic surgeon because he did not know the indications and contraindications for a spinal fusion in the neck?

43

Criterion-based referencing therefore is not appropriate for more than the very basic levels of professional practice. It is used for early professional examinations, for example, the Objective Structured Clinical Examination (OSCE), consisting of multiple examination stations with different tasks in each. Any attempt to utilise a pure criterion base for higher professional practice is inappropriate and veers back towards McNamara's Fallacy.

NORM-BASED

This is used to compare and contrast people who are supposedly at similar stages in their professional life and undertaking a similar workload. Marks are awarded and then plotted on a graph. If there are enough measurements then it will turn out to have a normal distribution.

With large enough numbers, the graph is independent of the level of questions and the knowledge base of the participants. A 'good year of participants' or easy questions can shift the curve to the right and a 'poor year' or difficult questions can move it to the left but nevertheless the curve remains. Grades, for example A to E, may be awarded by using the percentiles for instance the top 20% is graded A, the next 10% are graded B, etc. This system can certainly identify two extremes of the spectrum and may suggest the bottom 5% or 6% are 'underperforming'. However, it is subject to the same bias as mentioned under criterion-based assessment, and the most senior and experienced personnel may find themselves with a very low grade!

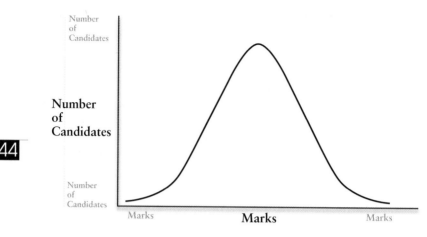

FIG.3 NORM-BASED ASSESSMENT

Such methods are again appropriate during the training grades but not at the high professional level. They are best for assessing a knowledge base but not particularly useful in determining technical capability or interpersonal skills. Assessment of a professional must test knowledge and technical skills along with attitudinal and interpersonal skills and must relate to day-to-day work practice.

SELF-BASED

Note this is not self-assessment! Rather, it is assessment based on an individual's job plan and role within the organisation.

In terms of senior medical staff, the overall pattern of the workload can be broken down under various headings using the acronym CREAM.

C Clinical workload. Looking particularly at knowledge base and competencies.

R Research activities covering work as a researcher, as an overseer of research or the ability to critically evaluate (this being the basis of evidence-based medicine).

E Educational activities both as teacher and learner.

A Audit activities both from a clinical point of view and an auditing of the complaints procedure. This includes a measure of interpersonal skills and general attitude or ethic.

M Management activities.

Very few job descriptions are alike and therefore the methods of assessment should reflect this.

There must be a base line against which progress can be measured, starting with a detailed job description coupled with the knowledge of what progress is to be expected over a period of time. Evidence must be gathered by both the appraiser and the appraisee regarding performance across the spectrum of the job. Frequently there may be a number of subsidiary lines of accountability for instance a Clinical Director for patient issues, a Postgraduate Dean with regards to teaching students or a university department for research activity. All need to input to give a rounded view which then can allow for detailed discussion about any specific issues which have been identified.

Since it is based on the appraisee, the job description and role along with any agreements which may have been made by both parties in the past, self-based assessment is the fairest method. It looks at both an individual and the environment, including resources and those elements which are going to be assessed are known in advance to both parties. This allows assessment which is valid for anyone in a post whether the most senior Professor or the newest House Officer. It deals with the real world and therefore is the basis of the appraisal process and ultimately any valid mechanism for assessment of professional practice.

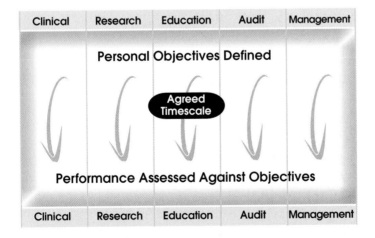

FIG.4 SELF-BASED ASSESSMENT

LIMEN-BASED
This is a very subjective method of assessment but can be very telling! If the

question is asked, for instance within a peer group of surgeons and anaesthetists, 'Can surgeons A, B, C & D competently perform a Laparoscopic Cholecystectomy?' Everyone may agree that at least A, B & C could do so. If the question is phrased another way 'Which of surgeons A, B, C & D would you ask to perform a Laparoscopic Cholecystectomy on you?' most will be able to rank by naming one individual whom they would ask and usually there is a fair degree of consensus. No examination is involved but possibly a lot of observation although unstructured and subjective. This is Limen-based assessment and is very frequent in society. From the award of Oscars for 'Best Actor' to voting in an election there is obviously a lot of room for bias but with increasing number of assessors, such biases are liable to be held to a minimum. This is referred to as the Principle of Triangulation.

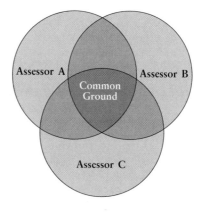

FIG.5 LIMEN-BASED ASSESSMENT

The greater the number of assessors or assessments that are made, the more likely there is to be an area of common ground moving towards 'reality'.

CONCLUSION

There are many types of assessment, many methods of carrying them out and numerous statistical analyses which can be applied. At the end of the day, when dealing with professional practice, the method of assessment needs to reflect the real world. It must be a valid reflection with reproducible results and not be so cumbersome that it is simply not feasible to carry out. The method which stands out for professional practice is self-based assessment. This method represents the favoured basis of the appraisal, assessment and ultimately revalidation processes and in order to minimise observer bias, objectives and standards must be developed and agreed in advance.

chapter 5
WHAT MAKES A GOOD APPRAISER

INTRODUCTION

IF APPRAISAL IS CENTRAL to any winning organisation then the role of the appraiser is vital to its success. Usually, an appraiser is the line manager and has a defined supervisory and/or training role with respect to the appraisee. In medical practice, this traditional relationship already exists with trainees. In contrast, the top levels are rather less hierarchical, if indeed at all, and the relationship is between peers with differing skills and expertise working as a unit.

An appraiser may not necessarily be the best clinician or most accomplished surgeon but needs to have a special skill in dealing with people. It is important that his peers respect him. He acts as a facilitator for discussion and a conduit linking the strategic and operational planners with those who carry them out. This allows two-way feedback, giving the opportunity for those in the front line to influence the strategic direction of the institution and the operational planning for the team. Good appraisers see their role as being more akin to that of a teacher, mentor, coach or facilitator rather than director, commander or judge. Appraisers identify with and encourage others to develop their own plans and achieve agreed objectives. They have to set high standards for themselves and be receptive to the views of others. Decisions taken with their peers during appraisal may well affect their own work practice, and if interpersonal grievances develop, these must not be allowed to develop into longer-term issues that hinder good professional practice. Hence the process must be handled very sensitively.

In this chapter we will look at those attributes that help to make a good appraiser.

KNOWLEDGE BASE

As with teaching, undoubtedly there are some who naturally make good appraisers. However, very few people would not benefit from some study of the process. The aims and objectives of appraisal should be clearly understood. Put simply, the exercise aims at reviewing progress with the appraisee against a set of objectives, identifying and acknowledging where success has been achieved as well as looking at those areas where difficulties were encountered. A personal development plan is jointly constructed, identifying individual learning needs and mechanisms for addressing them. A new set of objectives is then agreed. Accordingly a detailed knowledge of the strategic plan and the operational objectives for the organisation is required along with an understanding of why the organisation is heading in a particular direction.

From the point of view of the appraisee, the appraiser requires detailed knowledge at least of the job plan if not the intricacies of the job itself, and must keep abreast of new developments in the field and their implications. An appraiser therefore is continually in the process of self-development, learning, mastering information and analysing its relevance.

The appraiser must know and understand the system of appraisal and in particular, be aware of the various side effects of assessment that were discussed in chapter 4. The main role is that of a manager of people. There is a great temptation to become directly involved in tasks but working with a peer group of professionals the objective is to manage the action and not to get involved in the task. This can be very difficult and is why there needs to be a good grasp of the strategic vision and the operational objectives. Coupled with this, the appraiser needs to have some form of empowerment and the ability to agree plans in the sure expectation that once agreed these can be enacted. The appraiser must be able to think creatively around problems and understand that they may not have all the answers. Indeed, the appraisee should always be encouraged to suggest ways of achieving the objectives and may come up with ideas that the appraiser had not considered. Therefore the appraiser needs to form workable compromises, utilising a collaborative rather than a confrontational style. The key word is cooperation.

SKILLS

A number of skills and techniques are required to put the knowledge base into

48

action. The appraiser needs to be good at gathering evidence without being obtrusive and should be able to order that knowledge into a logical sequence.

Communication skills are vital especially active listening since it is important to concentrate on what is being said. Statements should be reflected back to the appraisee by paraphrasing to ensure accurate understanding. The technique is not to make statements but rather to generate questions since these demand reflection and answers. Such questions need to be open and probing, reflection being encouraged by starting with words such as:

49

> Why?
> Why not?
> What do you mean by?
> So what do you think that means?
> What might have made a difference, what other influences might have been operating?
> Is there anything about what I do that influences the way you carry out your job?

As far as possible the appraiser should give very little in the way of information but simply introduce the facts and any background information required to facilitate discussion. He should not overload the conversation with advice but rather help people to find their own way to a solution. Unless there is personal involvement with difficult issues, the appraiser's own feelings should be suppressed, avoiding any arguments unless there is a clear difference of opinion about performance. Such an opinion should be based on factual information, not conjecture, dealing if possible with the issue and not becoming personal. The appraiser should keep good eye contact and so the venue needs to be one with very little distraction.

Sometimes there is room for being a devil's advocate: challenging assumptions, giving alternative points of view or introducing experience from other places. The process is one of giving and receiving feedback. This leads to a joint problem solving exercise and as far as possible a win-win approach to the production of clear and 'SMART' objectives, i.e. objectives that are Specific, Measurable, Achievable (although demanding), Realistic and set within a certain Time frame.

Although appraisers need a clear understanding of the ultimate outcomes required, they need to display flexibility. They have to balance resilience towards the ultimate goals with sensitivity and tolerance in dealing with others. They need to listen, monitor what is being said and to a very great extent they need to be able to motivate (see chapter 3). They must be able to think creatively with attention to detail and certainly need good negotiating skills and the ability to be persuasive, since the end result must be realistically acceptable to the organisation. There must be clear planning with good time management and the ability to reach realistic and mutually accepted solutions. If tensions do arise they must be sensitively confronted since the generation of anger and frustration can easily fracture relationships within peer groups and cost a high price in future working relationships.

ATTITUDE

The attitude required is one of commitment to the process in terms of time, the effort required, the skill base and the belief that the process will benefit the appraisee as well as the organisation and ultimately patient care. Appraisers need to be honest, open and understand their own biases and attitudes. They need to have integrity and practice what they preach so if they are to be effective they must be good role models. They must realize that the process is aimed at raising the standards of performance and outcomes by increasing the appraisee's self-image since, if they have a greater sense of self-worth and confidence, they are must more likely to achieve more challenging objectives.

There is a temptation for an appraiser to view the appraisee as being in some way subordinate. Peer appraisal suggests discussion amongst equals and therefore demands a mutual respect of both people and their ideas, with the suggestions of the appraisee being paramount as long as they appear to be workable and in agreement with the goals of the organisation. Therefore, there needs to be agreement by both parties on the purpose of the appraisal and to have a clear focus on what it is intended to achieve.

INTERPERSONAL SKILLS

Interpersonal skills are exercised when someone initiates an action in order to achieve an aim which depends on the reaction of someone else. Everyone in the team will have their own objectives and within a peer group of professionals it is unlikely that individuals with be either inert or passive. A lot depends on how the appraisee respects the appraiser and vice versa. There will therefore be changes in the chemistry between them depending on the behaviour and reaction to the issues under discussion.

Understanding that different people have different interpersonal styles is a great deal to do with leadership. Sometimes it is necessary to be didactic especially in an emergency, but a good appraiser must have the ability to shift styles from simply giving feedback to being a coach or a mentor depending on what has to be done. This will depend very much on the level of seniority of the person they are working with and the level of knowledge for the particular task under discussion. Except in emergencies, such leadership should rarely be autocratic. It may be consultative, i.e. consulting and then making the decision, or democratic when the will of others may prevail.

A senior consultant being appraised may know a lot on a given topic and indeed even much more than the appraiser about specific clinical issues, but perhaps less for instance about teaching or research. Therefore, the way of handling such a person varies depending on the circumstances. No single leadership style is correct but anyone in a leadership role must be able to adapt as appropriate.

Since the object is to motivate the appraisee towards goals, if there are shared interests it is easier to move forward because of internal drive and an enjoyment of the process. If there is no such meeting of minds, then the skill of the appraiser is to understand the appraisee's needs, interests and concerns and by using this knowledge in combination with good negotiating skills, obtain agreement on key tasks.

CONCLUSION

Good appraisers have many characteristics. They must believe in what they are doing and be prepared to commit time and effort to develop their skills. They must have a clear understanding of how the process contributes to the objectives of the organisation and be capable of helping others play their role in the overall game plan. They must be good listeners and be particularly sensitive to understanding another's point of view. They should concentrate on facts and not emotions, with feedback being specific and positive as far as possible.

The main focus should be supportive, offering congratulations if a job is done well or gaining agreement that there is a problem and attempting to find a mutually agreeable solution.

It is a position of leadership with the style varying dependant on the situation, taking into account for instance the nature of the problem, the level of the seniority of the appraisee and their specific knowledge of the subject.

A good appraiser has the ability to be open to feedback, to reflect on practice and to be willing to adapt with the understanding that the role is to help both individuals and the organisation to achieve their objectives. The key task is that of motivation.

chapter 6
THE APPRAISAL AND ASSESSMENT PROCESS

INTRODUCTION

IN ORDER TO BE WORKABLE, the system must be simple to set up and maintain since over-elaboration will make it unwieldy from the point of view of the time involved and the likelihood of compliance by all parties. It has to be logical, well structured and adaptable so that it can be used across all the medical disciplines. Finally, it must be seen to be fair, to benefit individuals, and not be regarded simply as a management tool to keep staff in line.

The system must be staff centred, based on the job description and role definition. These are not quite the same thing. A job description is a definition of tasks using active verbs such as to plan, to develop, to prepare, to produce, to maintain and to monitor, i.e. stating what has to be done by the post holder, and why. Role definition is more about relationships, i.e. how an individual contributes to a team, a department or the organisation as a whole. An employee must have a clear picture of why they are employed, what results are expected and how they are going to be assessed. They also require to know for whom they are responsible and to whom they are accountable.

This chapter will look at the detail of the appraisal and assessment cycle, discussing who should carry it out, when and where it should be carried out and how to gather the necessary evidence for a meaningful discussion.

APPRAISAL AND ASSESSMENT CYCLE
ANALYSIS OF THE JOB

The process begins with the individual and requires detailed analysis of their job and their role within the organisation. It is important to realise at the outset that most clinicians will have duties covering much more than their clinical work.

The wide range of activities which may be required of senior medical staff may be paraphrased using the acronym CREAM (see page 44)

C   Clinical

R   Research

E   Education

A   Audit

M   Management

These all need to be considered in terms of process as well as task. For instance, 'Clinical' may be perceived as a check of outcomes against standards. In practice, it is more than that, including all aspects of clinical care from communication in outpatients through working in the ward environment to the way investigations and treatment are carried out.

'Research' activities most obviously relate to undertaking research and/or overseeing others. There is another very important aspect, namely critical reading and the ability to critically analyse research findings whether they are produced in a journal or at an international meeting. In other words it is how an individual integrates new knowledge into practice or indeed rejects it if inappropriate. This is the underlying philosophy of evidence-based medicine and strongly relates to the concept of clinical judgement.

'Educational' activities involve senior staff both as teacher and learner. Lifelong learning is essential with the fast pace of change in medical practice and therefore consultants must be able to show that they are continuing this process by learning themselves and also disseminating the information to others as teachers or at least the givers of information.

'Audit' requires participation in local, national or even international activities allowing reflection on practice. It is useless if it does not lead to growth and development. The main audit question is not 'Am I alright?' but rather 'No matter how good I am, is there any way I can improve?' It also requires honesty about practice and openness to suggestions for improvement. Again this covers more than clinical outcomes and, very importantly under this heading, comes the feedback from patients whether good or bad, and a positive attitude towards honest reflection on any points raised.

'Management' is regarded in its broadest sense. This may be management within a clinical setting involving patients, medical and paramedical staff, including overseeing clinics, wards and theatres, or more broadly, management of the Health Service in general. This may mean dealing with training and budgets for a whole hospital or more generally for the health of a population such as in public health medicine.

THE JOB PLAN

Individuals will have different expectations within each facet of work. Some **55** may do a lot of clinical work with very little management. Others may do a lot of research and less clinical work. It is therefore vital that the job is looked at 'in the round' and that each appraisal is tailored appropriately. The appraisal must address all areas of work and not concentrate solely on clinical issues, in order to give a balanced view of performance. If it becomes obvious that there is an imbalance or if new developments dictate a change in direction of a department or team, the outcome of the appraisal process may result in a change in emphasis on different aspects of the job plan or role.

EVIDENCE OF PERFORMANCE

Given what has been said, it is quite obvious that all the evidence is not in one place. The clinical evidence may involve national standards. Research and teaching may involve feedback from universities and the relevant post graduate authorities as well as feedback from the students. Audit may be very local and management activities may be on many levels requiring feedback from clinical colleagues and/or from other disciplines.

Information needs to be gathered from the five Ps: -

Personal	by an updated CV and portfolio.
Peers	both within and without the profession.
Patients	whose views must be actively sought.
Public	in general who at the end of the day set local and national agendas.
Professional Bodies	for instance the Royal Colleges, Universities and other institutions.

The Portfolio is a personal collection of any documents related to work practice. It would include, for example, current and previous personal development plans along with evidence such as papers or books to back up the information contained in the curriculum vitae. There could be examination results or letters of commendation from other official or unofficial sources. It should also contain adverse comments such as complaints, with a written reflection on how the complaint was resolved including lessons learned or consequent changes in practice.

The evidence of performance must be based on both hard and soft criteria. 'Hard' implies quantifiable factual data such as numbers, time and quantity levels. 'Soft' criteria are more qualitative in nature dealing with effectiveness, creativity, team building and general service. These are very difficult to quantify, but can be described in prose or rating scales.

How should this evidence be gathered? Some information will be routine, utilising a standard pro forma. This simply needs to be filled out by the appraisee prior to the interview and the answers assessed in a 'tick box' fashion. Unless there are any major discrepancies, no discussion is required. Examples of such items would be:

> Date of Birth
>
> Qualifications
>
> Confirmation of inclusion on the Specialist Register
>
> List of any restrictions to registration
>
> Details of employment including distinction awards
>
> Documented proof of continuing medical education activities as laid down by specialist bodies.

Other non-routine information gathering follows the agenda, thereby focusing the evidence required. Two or three opinions should be obtained under each heading to deal with the potential for any personal bias (see page 46).

The person who is asked for an opinion will depend on the topic in question. A '360-degree view' is commonly used, meaning someone in line management, a peer or other colleague with whom the individual works closely (which may include medical, nursing or other disciplines) and/or subordinate or a trainee. If possible, the names should be suggested by the appraisee and agreed with the appraiser. If there is a difference of opinion, each can then ask for opinions from their nominees. Such a system can be used throughout the grades from house officer to senior consultant.

The views of patients are extremely important. Their opinions are usually sought on an ongoing basis by an audit department or through any complaints procedure and these opinions must be readily available. If warranted, patients may also be canvassed directly for instance by phone or mail with regard to specific issues.

SETTING THE AGENDA

It is not possible to look at every facet of someone's job at every appraisal interview, nor is this desirable. Like any other form of assessment such as examinations, it is a process of sampling, weighted to those areas which are perceived to be of high importance such as clinical risk, or those that have been selected at a local or national level as a particular subject for audit.

57

Such topics are listed initially by the appraiser as a draft agenda which should contain four or five items. This should be sent to the appraisee six weeks in advance for agreement and the addition of one or two other topics the appraiser specifically wishes to discuss. This process should result in a final agenda of six to seven items, agreed and understood between the parties one month before the interview. This allows information to be obtained by both the appraiser and the appraisee for discussion at the meeting. It is very important that the appraisee in particular feels ownership of the agenda and that the interview is a genuine two-way process of discussion.

If a written personal development plan (see page 68) has been drawn up in the past, this should be discussed first in order to assess progress. Usually interviews are at yearly intervals, although with certain high-risk activities the frequency may be increased.

THE APPRAISAL INTERVIEW

The interview will be discussed in greater detail in the next chapter. At this stage it is important to emphasise that the interview should be convened as a meeting of peers and in a conducive environment. It is important that the whole emphasis is on growth and development of the appraisee by:

Reviewing past performance in specific areas

Identifying areas where growth and development can occur

Assessing training needs

Setting agreed targets for future performance

Identifying what will be required from the organisation to help achieve those targets.

Undoubtedly, some difficult issues will arise. These should be identified and isolated from other items and the rest of the agenda should be worked through first. Outstanding issues should then be tackled. It may be that issues require to be aired and revisited again a short time later, perhaps with the benefit of other evidence or with the help of third parties. The object is to seek cooperation, collaboration and compromise although undoubtedly, on occasions, confrontation may occur. Also, it is important to keep as far as possible to the problem at issue, rather than focus on the individual unless the problem becomes recurrent and entrenched.

POST-INTERVIEW ACTION

The courses of action agreed should be committed to paper and signed by those involved. This forms the basis of a personal development plan with agreed objectives and time frames . Tight timescales are particularly important if there is going to be a lot of change on behalf of the individual or the organisation. This is vital in order to keep the process moving forward.

FEEDBACK TO MANAGEMENT

Whether it is a particular issue or a generality, feedback is required to inform the management structure as appropriate, e.g. chief executive, clinical directors, university or educational supervisors. Obviously, with certain topics, confidentiality may be an issue but usually there is no problem and indeed most appraisees would actively wish their thoughts and ideas to be transmitted to others in order to inform the strategic cycle. As far as possible it should be accepted that unless there is prior agreement, the outcomes of confidential discussions should not be disclosed. However, it must be clear that certain issues, especially those involving any risk to patients, cannot be kept purely confidential. The reasons for a breach of confidentiality by either side must be explicit, and as far as possible be dealt with at the time of the interview. Such issues should only be shared with other parties on a 'need to know' basis.

FEEDBACK WITH THE APPRAISEE

Feedback to the appraiser is vital. There may be specific feedback required on particular topics, for instance agreement to adapt a budget or approval for a new development. Further, appraisers themselves are not acting in a vacuum and feedback on the appraiser's performance and how they carried out the appraisal interview needs to be obtained. This is to avoid potential conflicts and the development of too rigid a hierarchy that may be inappropriate amongst peers. It also helps to engage any personal biases the appraisers may have.

Finally, this feedback also involves a look at the job and role of the appraisee and any potential conflicts or changes that may be required. This feeds back into the appraisee's job description and role, taking us back to the beginning of the cycle.

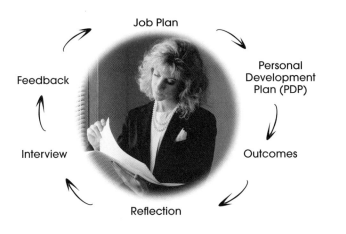

FIG.I THE APPRAISAL CYCLE

WHO SHOULD DO THE APPRAISING?

In an institution of any size, one individual cannot carry out all the appraisals. Even with a one-hour interview, it takes a further two to three hours both to prepare and to deal with any issues. A reasonable maximum for any appraiser is between six and eight staff and therefore the process needs to be cascaded so that it involves everyone within the organisation.

All senior staff need to be trained to carry out appraisals. They may be appraising their peers, other full-time staff of non-consultant grade and also those in training. In turn they will be appraised themselves and therefore there must be uniformity about the system and there needs to be clarity about what the system is supposed to achieve. In particular there is the importance of taking an overall view of a job plan and how to gather appropriate evidence. The basic principles about how to go about agreeing objectives must be fully understood. The process must be kept as objective as possible because it can tend to become very personal, especially with a '360 degree' appraisal involving line management, peers, perhaps of other disciplines, and trainees. In fact, feedback from colleagues is one of the most valuable tools if it is truly objective. However, if such feedback is perceived to be in the nature of a personal attack this can completely destroy relationships within the unit and the team may be impossible to rebuild if trust is lost.

The role of the appraiser is extremely important and it is fully discussed in chapter 5.

WHEN AND WHERE?

Appraisals need to be conducted at least annually and should if possible link into the planning cycle of the organisation. This allows for:

> Feedback into the strategic planning process
>
> Evaluation of performance against operational targets
>
> Setting of new operational targets.

A properly carried out appraisal is a positive process and it is not something to be set aside and only handled when absolutely necessary. Objectives are set with clear standards, agreed methods of assessment and a time frame. At the interview it must be decided whether or not a particular topic will need to be revisited and if so exactly when. If the appraiser is acting as a mentor or a coach this may be more frequent and perhaps some of the follow-up to appraisal can be informal without the necessity of going through the full structure of an appraisal interview. A discussion over coffee, in the corridor or via a chance meeting may be quite sufficient but may require to be documented.

Other topics, usually those requiring a large change, may need to be more formally appraised. The normal cycle is annual but for specific points, three or four monthly reviews may be required. It is always advisable to keep some record on file, but these more frequent appraisals may not need to include the detail of the feedback from a full interview. It may simply be noted that the actions which were contemplated had been carried out by a specific date.

CONCLUSION

The appraisal and assessment process is a cycle where the interview is the central component. The appraisal and assessment process is a normal function and an integral part of management at all levels and should concern everyone in an organisation. It looks at teams and individual performance and is continuous. It gives feedback to the organisation about how the strategic plans are being carried out in practice and allows it to plan ahead. The whole process must be simple and those running it need to be trained and skilled in what they do. The outcomes of the cycle are presented in a written format, detailing clear objectives with agreed time frames.

These documents, over time, for example over four or five different appraisal cycles, will give a clear insight into the breadth of performance and therefore powerfully contribute to any process of revalidation. Where these indicate progress and achievement without any problems then revalidation should be virtually automatic. Likewise, they show where there have been problems and where these have satisfactorily addressed. However, the system will also highlight areas where there have been problems that have not been resolved. Indeed, if there have been any issues relating to patient safety, it allows active steps to be taken when these arise rather than waiting for a formal revalidation exercise which may not be due for several years.

The appraisal process therefore is very much for the benefit of both doctor and patient. As such, the process needs to be checked and evaluated on a regular basis, probably by external audit. It should be seen to deliver results in line with the goals of the organisation, thereby serving the organisation and ultimately the patient as well as protecting professional staff.

The detail of how to set up and carry out the interview will be discussed in chapter 7

61

chapter 7

THE APPRAISAL INTERVIEW AND PRODUCTION
OF PERSONAL DEVELOPMENT PLANS

INTRODUCTION

THE INTERVIEW IS CENTRAL to the whole system of appraisal. It can be an extremely personal process between individuals and if it is done well, following a logical and structured plan, it should be empowering for all involved. If it is not handled correctly, it can become disorganised and even confrontational leading to the demoralisation and demotivation of both parties.

Individuals should be appraised against their job description and previous personal development plans. A well written job description ensures that the appraisee has a clear picture of job purpose and objectives, and what outcomes are expected. As far as the role within the organisation is concerned, they need to be clear about the line management structure, to whom they are accountable and who is accountable to them. Whilst those in training may have a single line of accountability, senior medical personnel may have more than one, for instance for clinical or management activities. A clear statement of the job and the role means that the appraisal process can be much more objective. Outcomes may be judged against external criteria thereby diminishing any subjective bias.

The outcome of the interview should be that both parties have reflected on an evidence-based discussion of performance against agreed standards and that an action plan has been developed to both encourage further developments and to deal with any deficiencies which may have arisen. It is equally important that time is spent acknowledging and encouraging good performance. Finally, a new personal development plan should be produced laying down objectives for the coming year.

The interview is a personal process and, in common with any form of counselling, depends a great deal on interpersonal relationships. It should be conducted in a positive, supportive manner that encourages full participation by both parties. The interview should provide a solid base for the future with a joint (and occasionally three way if specific expertise is required) approach to problem solving where required. A relationship of mutual respect between the appraiser and appraisee is important and at the same time there has to be recognition of the legitimacy and authority of the process.

FIG. I. THE PLANNING CYCLE FOR APPRAISAL AND ASSESSMENT

Successful outcomes demand that adequate attention is paid to all three stages namely preparation for the interview, the conduct of the appraisal interview itself and the prompt completion of post interview tasks culminating in the production of an agreed personal development plan.

PRE-INTERVIEW PROCEDURES

Six weeks prior to the interview, the appraiser should agree the date, time and venue with the appraisee and ensure that both have a copy of the current job description and the most recent personal development plan. The appraiser must make himself aware of any specific issues which have been highlighted for discussion. These may be personal to the appraisee or more general issues which have been raised by local or more national policies. Finally, the appraiser requires a clear understanding of both strategic and operational objectives as they pertain to the appraisee in order to work out the general thrust of the personal development plan and also how they are empowered to help that process happen.

Agreement should be reached with the appraisee regarding who will be asked to contribute to the process. Normally input should be sought from a peer, a subordinate and others to whom the appraisee is responsible for part of their job, for example a university or a Royal College.

65

The first item for discussion will be progress against the current personal development plan, and a draft agenda including this item should be written detailing a further four to five issues. The plan and the agenda should be sent to the appraisee, asking for comments. At this time in most instances the appraisee should then provide his portfolio and a short written submission of progress against the personal development plan. The portfolio must contain details of performance on the whole range of clinical and non-clinical activities as laid down by the General Medical Council in the United Kingdom. It includes the handling of critical incidents, complaints with a statement of reflection and lessons learned *(Revalidating Doctors - Ensuring Standards, Securing the Future, GMC 2000)*. The appraisee may also suggest one or two points which they wish to discuss. This should result in an agreed agenda at least one month before the interview.

Once the information has been received, the appraiser should spend some time considering performance over the year asking questions such as:

How well has the appraisee achieved his objectives?

How well have any improvements, development or training plans been carried out?

Is there evidence of exemplary performance?

Where has performance been weak?

What factors have influenced the performance and are they within the control of the appraisee?

What future developments are required?

What are the appraisee's strengths and what objectives would be challenging?

What resources (finance, training, time) are required?

Do I need to discuss the matter with anyone else?

Do I have the necessary authority?

Appraisal by ambush is not acceptable. Both sides can then start to collate any supporting data as required so the next few weeks prior to interview, any specific issues raised in the portfolio can be brought out into the open and shared so that there are no surprises suddenly sprung at the meeting.

During this time, the appraisee should also be reflecting:

> What have I achieved over the last year?
>
> What do I wish to achieve over the next few years?
>
> What training and resources will I need?
>
> Would it require a change in my job description?
>
> Where has my performance been weak?
>
> Why was there a problem?
>
> What would be required to remedy it?
>
> What guidance and help would benefit me?

By the time of the meeting, both parties should have clear ideas of the main issues and what they expect to achieve.

THE INTERVIEW

The date, time and venue should be organised well in advance and confirmed in writing. All arrangements should be acceptable to both parties and should not be changed unless completely unavoidable, thereby demonstrating commitment to the process. The appraiser should not carry out more than two appraisals in one day as they require concentration and focus and can be very tiring.

Light refreshment should be available and attention paid to the surroundings. The room should be comfortable and well lit. It is appropriate that both parties sit on the same side of the desk or table and neither should sit with their back to the light nor facing a window as this can be very distracting. Secretaries should ensure that there are no interruptions; telephones and bleeps should be switched off. Both parties should keep notes and responsibility for recording the process should be mutually agreed. A flip chart may be a useful aid.

At the very beginning of the interview there should be an agreement about confidentiality and specifically, under what circumstances confidentiality cannot be assumed by either side. This particularly relates to any issue that may compromise patient safety. The agreement should also extend to methods of storing any paperwork generated in the process.

The first item on the agenda should always be 'Any Other Business'. This allows the level of importance of such items to be gauged right at the beginning and decisions can be made whether to slot it in or defer the issue completely. The interview will last around one hour. It can be intense and is not sensible to start to discuss a new issue that may not have been properly researched by both sides.

The core business is a review of the previous personal development plan. This starts with the objectives, concentrating on the performance that was expected and not on any extraneous issues. The conversation should be freely flowing and not a series of staccato questions or answers, although it is important that discussions are kept on track with a definite purpose and do not meander too far off the topic.

It is crucial that any examples are concrete, i.e. what was done, what should have been done or what someone else thinks should have been done. There need to be comparisons with previously agreed standards and the key word is reflection. The appraisee should give their statements first and highlight achievements both of themselves and their team. The standards used for comparison must relate to the everyday work environment, in other words they must be valid for the circumstances. They must also be sufficiently important to make a difference to the success or failure of the outcome and be within control of the person or team doing the job. There must be some flexibility allowing for changes in priorities and environments when the circumstances change.

If objectives have not been achieved, then the reasons why this is so need to be teased out. What has inhibited performance? Was it within the remit of the person doing the job? Was the problem with external sources, including lack of resource or management deficiencies? The question also needs to be asked why these were not addressed and actions taken during the appraisal period. The conversation needs to concentrate on future developments, areas for improvement and how that improvement can be achieved and it must be emphasised that time should be spent discussing achievements and strengths and not simply leaping from point to point discussing methods of improvement. The appraiser should remember that their job is motivation (see chapter 3).

Any feedback to the appraisee should be specific, factual, non emotional and directly work related. It will include a two-way review of feedback from peers and others to whom the appraisee is accountable. If criticism is necessary it should not be obscured but clearly related to performance and behaviour, not personality.

THE PERSONAL DEVELOPMENT PLAN - SETTING OBJECTIVES

A Personal Development Plan is a performance agreement that defines expectations by setting 'SMART' objectives (specific, measurable, achievable, relevant and timely) for the individual and his team, the work to be done and the results to be achieved along with appropriate timescales (see Appendix A). It also clarifies the skills and competencies that are necessary together with any training required. Where appropriate, it identifies any help that is required from other sources. The plan should result from an agreement on clear objectives with the appropriate standards. Where standards are not already prescribed, there should be discussion regarding the setting and monitoring of appropriate standards detailing how they are going to be measured, when and by whom. There may need be a template for the achievement of the objectives although how detailed this is depends on the level of experience of the appraisee. For senior clinicians, it is much more appropriate to agree the way forward in general terms, then leave them to sort out the detail. With trainees, more direct coaching and advice may be necessary. However, even with senior staff, more specific plans are required if it is a matter of utilising considerable resources. These may have to fit a particular sequence or time frame and require provision of training either for the appraisee or others, particularly if a team is involved.

Performance ratings are not a particularly good idea. These seem to be convenient measures and may be able to identify exceptional performance or marked underperformance. Unfortunately they are inclined to be subjective in a lot of respects, and it is difficult to be consistent and add all the elements of the discussion up in a single number. Obviously, really poor performance must be highlighted, as should exceptional performance but between these extremes, the gradation within a peer group, can be counter-productive. For instance, someone who is performing well in a good group may be 'average' for the group. When compared to others in different groups the performance may actually be very high. Labelling them as 'average' may come across as demeaning and could result in demotivation.

The process should build on the appraisee's strengths and present them with challenges they can meet. There is no point in staying in the comfort zone.

Objectives have to be realistic and achievable in the time frame, but at the same time, must push at the limits so that effort is required. Without this, there is no expansion and growth, no movement and consequently no feeling of success.

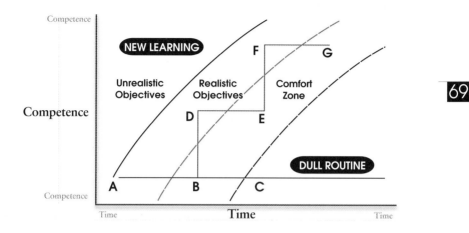

FIG. 2 THE PROFESSIONAL GROWTH CURVE:

   SETTING REALISTIC BUT CHALLENGING OBJECTIVES

The Comfort Zone is not static, but rather moves with time. Referring to figure 2, someone starting at point A, a difficult area, should, after training and experience, enter their Comfort Zone at point B. If they do not add to their competency and strive for improvement, then they will leave the zone at point C where everything becomes routine and eventually boring and demotivating.

It is necessary once one has entered the comfort zone to set higher objectives (point D), stretching an individual's performance until that level itself moves back into the Comfort Zone. Repetition forms a series of steps, and the upward movement gives the feeling of success and achievement. To simply arrive and then move no further is of no ultimate benefit to the person concerned or the organisation.

The discussions during the interview are based on evidence of performance in all facets of work. There should be confirmation of participation in continuing professional development, clinical governance activities and perhaps training in emergency treatment if appropriate. There should also be demonstration that the doctor has tried to maintain successful professional relationships with his own team, with other peers, with trainees and particularly with patients.

Throughout, a clear written record needs to be taken especially of decisions made. The appraiser must be persistent in getting specific answers. An objective 'to improve' is not specific enough. The decisions must be checked by summarising and getting agreement.

The personal development plan should list objectives in line with those of the organisation. They need to be challenging, taking full account of the ability of the person concerned, their aspirations and their accountability within their team or organisation. They must be realistic, with clear time frames and have some idea of priority for instance, high, medium and low, and with agreed success criteria in terms or performance and quality. There must be some idea of specific actions which must be taken either by the appraisee or the organisation with appropriate standards and methods of assessment.

Objectives are in the nature of a contract, and occasionally they can be stated in terms of 'if the organisation produces a particular piece of equipment, then I will agreed to ...' or, 'if there will be financial assistance for training, then we will ...'. Any controversial issues need to be 'problem-solved', preferably by gaining cooperation through collaboration or compromise rather than confrontation. The latter will be discussed in the next chapter which considers difficult issues. During the interview, it is essential for the appraiser to keep calm and remain assertive. If the appraisee states that something will not or cannot work, then ask why or in what way the task is inappropriate or unfair. What prevents them from doing what they have to do? Often, with professionals, they actually know what to do but there is some block to doing what they know. Try the 'feel, felt, found' approach, i.e. 'I know how you feel, I/others felt the same way too but they found that in practice...'. This approach can help to engage individuals so that they will try to move in the appropriate direction.

POST-INTERVIEW

Agreements reached during the interview need to be formalised and written out to become the personal development plan. This may be done either by the appraiser or preferably the appraisee, but should be agreed and co-signed within one or two weeks. During that time, some issues may need clarification but it is very important that this is done with a short time-scale in order to keep up momentum. There also needs to be feedback to the appraiser in terms of both the process and the outcomes of the interview. Both parties must state whether they agree the outcomes or if they disagree with them, giving the reasons why and allowing if necessary for an appeal to the appraiser's line manager. Finally, the plan is distributed to those who have a legitimate interest, again by agreement with both parties as far as possible, unless of course it involves one of the confidentiality issues which were discussed at the beginning.

The records should normally be developed in triplicate, one copy to the appraisee and two to the appraiser, for filing in the personnel department, subject to local agreement. One of the two records with the appraiser is maintained as a permanent record of all agreements, and the other perhaps used as a reminder to the appraisee immediately before their next appraisal.

CONCLUSION

The appraisal interview is central to the process and must be professionally planned and conducted. It consists of a review of performance against the personal development plan and a review of the job role and description. It should highlight achievements and identify the reasons behind any problem areas with a view to developing an action plan to enhance future performance. Other specific areas highlighted by the organisation or the appraisee should also be discussed with similar intention.

The process should be objective, focusing on concrete events with appropriate evidence from reports, surveys, feedback from peers, other staff, management, universities, students and indeed patients. Objective feedback from colleagues is extremely valuable provided it is truly objective. Also, a careful discussion on the handling of and learning from any complaints can facilitate progress. The outcome is the production of a negotiated personal development plan with specific, measurable, achievable, relevant and timely (SMART) objectives which serve to guide performance within the overall aims of the organisation. It should include some form of action plan including any necessary details especially where it impacts on others or requires the use or resources. The key is collaboration and negotiated compromise and to steer away as far as possible from any confrontation. Unfortunately, difficult issues must sometimes be faced and the techniques for dealing with them will be discussed in Chapter 8.

chapter 8
DEALING WITH DIFFICULT ISSUES

INTRODUCTION

THE OVERALL AIM of the appraisal system is to improve performance and the *sine qua non* is an honest evaluation of strengths and weaknesses. This is extremely difficult to achieve in an atmosphere of confrontation, recrimination and reprisal, but, as well as recognition of success, the system must be able to highlight difficult areas and develop a plan to overcome them.

In the case of problem doctors, there is usually a history of difficult behaviour or underperformance that is well known at some level within the organisation, particularly amongst their peer group. Human nature being as it is, contentious issues are sometimes ignored hoping they will go away. In the longer term this results in ongoing poor performance, a lack of productivity, non-achievement of objectives and often leads to difficult working relationships. All of this can compromise patient safety and is totally unacceptable.

Problems must therefore be made explicit and addressed as early as possible. Obviously it is preferable if difficulties are first recognised by the appraisee. If not, the appraiser will need to define the issues in such a way that they are acknowledged by the appraisee.

The next stage is to establish and understand the underlying reasons, looking coldly, dispassionately but empathetically at what is happening or what is likely to happen, without attaching any blame. Are these reasons intrinsic to the parties concerned or at least within their control. If not, who does have control? Is the problem personal or does it have its roots in an organisational issue such as lack of resources or management, or with the prioritisation of those resources that are available?

74   The key to solving difficult issues within the appraisal system is to gain cooperation leading to collaboration or compromise. This requires a concentration on facts, avoiding as far as possible any semblance of an attack on an individual as a person. Once emotions are involved to any high degree, it is much more difficult to achieve a resolution without loss of face on either side.

Direct confrontation will be necessary on occasions but there is no reason why it should become aggressive. At the end of the day, if the appraisal system does not result in the necessary changes or improvements then there may be a disciplinary issue, but that should be seen as a total failure of the appraisal process.

We will now deal with methods of clearly identifying the problems and then look at specific and effective solutions.

IDENTIFICATION OF THE PROBLEM

Performance can only be improved if problems are clearly identified and agreed between the parties, underlying contributory factors explored and consideration given jointly to how these might be addressed. This requires factual information and a decision as to whether the root cause is related to individuals or the organisation in terms of its resources and management or any combination of the two.

The General Medical Council states that the responsibility is on the individual doctor to realize when performance is deficient. In reality it requires cooperation from everyone else including colleagues, employers and the supporting agencies. That is the power of appraisal and a continuing process of feedback is necessary to ensure that the practitioner is displaying good communication and interpersonal skills, is keeping up-to-date with his knowledge base and technical skills and that all of these are complemented by the environment in which he operates.

Unlike the hierarchical management structures within most organisations, in many of the professions and particularly in medicine, the management structure is almost flat. Most consultants are relatively autonomous and have only recently been made accountable to a Clinical Director, who is often a peer.

The organisational system which has evolved in medicine in the United Kingdom, considers the Clinical Director as first and foremost a manager and he may not necessarily be the best clinician. This can lead to problems if there is a disagreement over an issue of clinical judgement in that the Clinical Director could be, for example, a general surgeon with responsibility for the appraisal of an ENT consultant. In such circumstances it is vital that the problem is identified and defined. Resolution may require the involvement of a third party, perhaps an ENT consultant from another hospital, to help resolve the disagreement.

Continuing poor performance leads to poor clinical outcomes and must therefore be addressed. This is best achieved in an atmosphere of openness and frank discussion in order to reach a satisfactory conclusion. With formal assessment, when problems are raised there is liable to be a lot of emotion and defensiveness and therefore conversations may not be as open as they must be to get to the core of an issue and to gain resolution. A properly constituted appraisal system provides the best opportunity to achieve a win-win solution.

THE ANATOMY AND PHYSIOLOGY OF PROBLEM SOLVING

The anatomy of problem solving refers to the formula or structure for problem solving and the physiology to the underlying processes.

The formula outlined below for dealing with problems relates to individual performance or behavioural issues. With slight alteration these principles may be followed when the problem relates to organisational management or resources.

In truth everyone sometimes has an off day, but if unacceptable behaviour is an ongoing feature then it needs to be addressed. This relates not only to poor performance due to lack of knowledge or skill but also performance issues of an attitudinal nature such as habitual lateness, not completing tasks or a failure to comply with instructions. Relationship difficulties with patients and/or colleagues is another example. Dealing with these matters is particularly urgent if there is any question of compromising patient safety.

The formula is:

> Clearly state the problem or issue.
>
> Provide evidence. Innuendo is not sufficient.
>
> Describe the physical and or the emotional effects it is having on the appraisee and those around them.
>
> Describe the consequences for the appraisee or their patients if there is no change, including any sanctions that may eventually occur.
>
> Invite a response and make suggestions for the way forward.
>
> Either agree these or put forward other suggestions, identifying the likely outcomes of such actions.
>
> If the situation does not improve in spite of previous agreements or if there is a refusal to co-operate, restate the problem and ask for an explanation as to why the behaviour is continuing.
>
> Finally, if necessary, follow through with the consequences.

It can be seen that, at every step, the opportunity exists for discussion in an attempt to find an agreed way forward. Steps one and two are particularly vital. The clear facts should be given with the evidence in an objective and non-emotional manner. Success comes from trying to bring out the best in people and not attempting to push them into submission.

The physiological or process aspect of problem solving relates to helping to change someone's ideas or perspectives. There are three phases:

> Unfreezing.
>
> Instigating change.
>
> Refreezing.

Unfreezing is usually a slow process and is the reason why it is most difficult to change someone who is already set in their ways. Any trainer will recognize those who have come to his department with preformed ideas! A change in habit may take up to three months to become ingrained whereas a new habit may become established in half that time.

The unfreezing process requires a change in external perceptions. If an individual is simply told what they are doing is wrong and instructed to alter their habits, they will tend to become defensive, therefore it is best to try and avoid a direct challenge. Rather they need to be convinced of the need to change. People generally act rationally from their own point of view and will change if they are motivated to do so. Most professionals will learn if they can be helped to believe in change. In the appraisal process therefore, it is at times wise not to be too direct.

To begin with, it is best to acknowledge accomplishments, inviting them to identify any difficulties and how these have been overcome. Then they should be asked to identify problems that have not been addressed. If the issue of concern to the appraiser has not been raised, it can be introduced with statements such as 'there is one topic I need to address with you' or 'there is a particular question I need to ask' and then point out the difficulties in the present situation. If appraisal is properly conducted and all the evidence has been produced then it should not be too difficult. Indeed, the appraisee should have some idea that the topic is going to be broached from pre-interview correspondence.

The second phase is to instigate the change. It is most important that appraisees have time to reflect on the situation and attempt to find the solutions themselves. They may be helped by supplying them with the appropriate evidence in terms of data or standards, as used in evidence-based medicine. If they do come to conclusions themselves, they are much more likely to be committed as the result is internalised. If solutions are suggested when they are not ready to receive them the likely answers are 'yes but' or 'it is all very well but' or 'however, in my experience'. With most of the problems appraisees will have a lot of background knowledge and so it is better to try and use this to seek a solution rather than allowing them to use their experience to concentrate on possible problems with a solution suggested by someone else.

Active listening is required, looking specifically for common ground and as far as possible avoiding any 'blame culture'. The solution they come up with may not be the same one the appraiser brought to the table but if it is realistic, practical and sustainable it should be agreed.

The refreezing process takes time, six weeks to three months as detailed before. Therefore, follow-up discussions should occur at least at those intervals in order to make sure that the change has occurred. Once such agreements are made they should be put in writing and signed.

INDIVIDUAL PERFORMANCE ISSUES

The first task is to decide whether or not the problem is specific to the person concerned. Is it indeed part of their job description or role? If so, do they fully understand that it is and the standards that are expected?

Assuming it is accepted that the problem is legitimately to do with a person's own performance then deficiencies need to be analysed under three headings:

A knowledge problem. Did they know how to do it? For example, errors and delays in diagnosis or the use of outmoded treatments.

A skill or competence problem. Could they do it? Or are there technical errors in their performance.

An attitude problem. Despite having the knowledge and skill, did they carry out the task to the best of their ability? They may have difficulties in working with a team or communicating with colleagues or patients.

It is important to know which of these is most relevant. The first two, involving gaps in knowledge or skill, are relatively easily tackled through training and possibly coaching and mentoring. Attitudinal problems can be more difficult to address and may become a disciplinary issue but it is best to try and deal with these at an early stage within the appraisal system.

In general terms, it is much easier to work with people who have problems with factual information or skill levels. Unfortunately, these are rarely isolated and nearly always have some emotional element since no self-respecting professional wishes to be thought of as incompetent in his job. The problem is often the sheer pace of change in modern medicine. It may well be that someone with 20 years experience was initially a very sound and skilled clinician. Their practice may indeed have been up-to-date a number of years ago but, because they themselves have not moved on, they have gradually fallen behind their peers, and do not recognise that they have become old fashioned in their approach.

The life cycle of a surgical procedure is illustrated in figure 1. Between A and B the procedure is being learned. From B to C there is a rapid expansion in its use and the practitioner is developing experience. Enthusiasm with the technique can lead to overuse. At point C more caution is introduced as potential problems become apparent and there is a reflection on its place in surgical practice. From D to E more experience is gained and the technique becomes more commonplace although possibly not to the initial levels. From

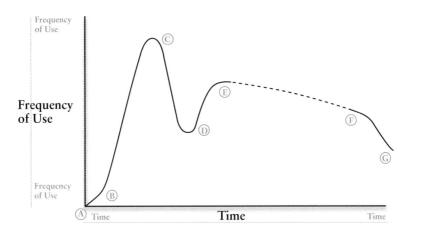

FIG.1 THE LIFE CYCLE OF A SURGICAL PROCEDURE

E to F it is in routine practice until it starts to become superseded by new techniques or perhaps drug therapies. The technique may now become 'old fashioned', and needs to be re-evaluated (G). Some practitioners may not recognise the changed situation or find difficulty in altering their practice. The benefit of the appraisal system is that it enables such matters to be dealt with early, hopefully by a small group on a 'need to know' and supportive basis. Indeed, most would welcome this approach over the trauma of a more public audience. A surgical procedure is used as an example, but the cycle applies equally to other areas of medical practice.

FIG.2 THE LEARNING CYCLE

Insight is a prerequisite for change. If the appraisee does not recognize the problem, in other words is unconsciously incompetent, then the first step is to move them along the line to conscious incompetence. This requires objective evidence and it is better if the practitioner reflects on his own performance and is given a chance to judge outcomes against agreed standards. This is particularly valuable in clinical work and should come from the process of audit.

When first confronted with the necessity for change, it is not unnatural for individuals to be defensive and to go through a process of denial. Poor performance may be because the knowledge and skill was not present to begin with, has become out of date or that the individual is attempting to operate beyond his competency level. Whatever the reason, then the process of moving from unconscious incompetence to conscious incompetence can be painful but it is a journey that must be undertaken.

The appraiser must understand the process of learning.

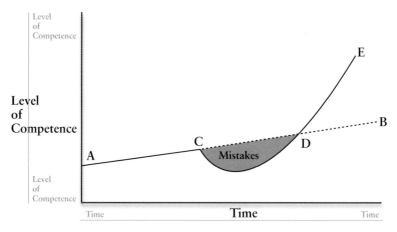

FIG.3 THE DEVELOPMENT OF COMPETENCE

This learning process is diagrammatically outlined in figure 3. At first there is shock when confronted with the situation. This may be followed by denial of any need to change or to learn new techniques. The third step is an emotional defence which usually manifests as anger. If they manage to work through the anger they usually look for some form of compromise 'do I really need to make all these changes and will some of them not do?' Finally, there is the stage of acceptance when they are then open and responsive to offers of help. This whole process can be emotionally draining which is not surprising since it mirrors the bereavement cycle.

The important area is between C and D on the graph. Here, because of learning the new skill, competence may indeed drop and this whole area under the line is characterized by mistakes. It is most important that peers and trainers understand the learning cycle to mentor and coach the learner through the change. Internal drive at this point is very important to help someone continue on the path. They must be helped to see that performance can be improved (point E) and that the end state is better than the original, thus making it worthwhile to go through the process. Insensitivity, denigration and confrontation is totally counterproductive when someone is trying to learn. They must be guided and supported at both a practical and emotional level. Confidentiality as far as possible is a key issue and there must be clear ground rules for any discussion outside the close circle.

81

Around the point D they become consciously competent in that they can carry out the procedure providing they think about it, with perhaps some guidance. By the time they reach point E they have become unconsciously competent and have mastered the skill or knowledge base.

People have different orientations as regards their attitude towards process and task.

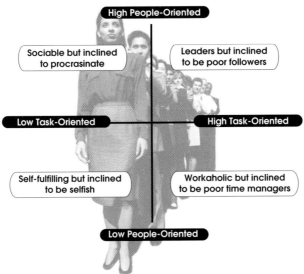

FIG.4 PEOPLE-V-TASK ORIENTATION

It is of paramount importance that the appraiser recognizes his own orientation and realizes the impact it has on others. High task and low people orientation are workaholics who can actually be quite destructive. Teamwork requires socialization and an understanding that different individuals have different orientations. This is why it takes a group time to learn to work together. The group will:

Form

Storm

Norm

Perform

On first meeting, a group enters a brief honeymoon period with most members being on their best behaviour. It may then storm where there is some element of disruption as everyone finds their level and works out relationships within the group. Eventually it settles down so that everyone understands their role (norm) and only then can the group properly perform.

Organisations may feel they would like to employ workaholics who have a high throughput but they can greatly upset the dynamics of a team. Likewise there are problems with high task, high people-orientated individuals who usually take on a leadership role and can become resentful if they feel they are being relegated to a subsidiary position. Those with high people and low task-orientation are very sociable and tend to procrastinate. Those with low people and low task-orientation can be quite selfish in nature and have difficulties working with a group. It is important to note that orientation can differ at different times and individuals will vary. It is really only when they become extreme in any of the areas that difficulties arise. However, an understanding of their prime orientation does help when the appraiser is trying to motivate (see chapter 3).

INDIVIDUAL BEHAVIOURAL ISSUES

Behavioural issues are more difficult and require considerable interpersonal skills. Some of the common ones will be discussed below with some specific suggestions for dealing with them.

BULLYING BEHAVIOUR

Behavioural problems are usually extremes of the norm. Bullying for example, is an extreme attempt at leadership. There is the laudable element of competition and drive to win but it becomes extreme when it is done at the expense of others without listening to their point of view. Often everyone is aware of the bullying behaviour but no one has tackled it. Indeed it may well be evident towards the appraiser, either on an ongoing basis in the workplace or during the appraisal interview.

The appraiser must decide in advance how to confront the issue and should decide a bottom line of what is acceptable and what outcome is required from the appraisee.

During the interview the only way to gain respect is to stand up to a bully. They should be addressed formally. They should not be allowed to interrupt when others are speaking and should be asked not to raise their voice. When they do make a point, the appraiser should reflect it to show that it has been heard and then give his own point of view, speaking calmly and confidently. Their name should be used frequently to gain attention and the interview conducted along the lines of the formula on page 76

conducted along the lines of the formula on page 76

INFLEXIBILITY

Inflexibility is an extreme of decision-making. Having made their own decision, inflexible clinicians tend to resist new ideas and have a rigid closed mind. The starting point is to acknowledge their point of view and listen to their precise thoughts on the matter. They can be very forthright in defending their position and therefore it is best to try and avoid a head on challenge. Try instead to discuss and find a shared vision for the future and have them offer ways of moving towards it. If you suggest a solution ask their advice and once you get some agreement try to get commitment and ask them how they are going to contribute to the outcome so that they do have ownership. Any follow-up should be in writing.

EGOCENTRIC BEHAVIOUR

The extreme of social skills is showing off to draw attention to themselves. They are happy in a group situation providing they get the lion share of the attention, either within the group or when the group is presenting itself to the outside world. The first step is to allow them to talk and ask for their suggestions in relation to a particular problem. This gets them to focus on specific issues. Ask their advice and perhaps show them where others have tried and gone wrong. When they come up with a reasonable solution, with or without help, again, get commitment with a time frame emphasizing the positive aspects of rewards and credits. If they get into difficulty, do not say 'I told you so' but rather try to empathize and determine with them why things went wrong then emphasize the support available and particularly the need for team support to help them achieve.

AVOIDANCE OF RESPONSIBILITY

There are those who will not take responsibility. They are the extreme of team players but have become very passive and the appraiser must try to find out the reasons why. Have they ever had the opportunity to lead before and are they frightened of moving ahead themselves? Do they feel disempowered or is it related to a previous unsuccessful experience? They need to feel supported and are not being asked to put their head on a block. They need to be given easily achievable objectives to begin with and gain positive feedback, with acknowledgement for their achievements. These objectives therefore need to be SMART (specific, measurable, achievable, relevant and timely) and they need an emphasis on team actions so that they feel supported and that there is a safety net around them.

84

Others simply opt out and refuse to take on a responsibility they are quite capable of managing. At the end of the day such underperformance has to be brought out into the open. Their work is usually substandard and they have an expectation that others will solve the problems or cover for them. They can become the whingers, becoming overly critical or dismissive towards others. They also have a habit of getting into unresolved conflict and do not work well within a team.

The most important corrective action is not to shy away from the issue. At the end of the day one must face up to the problem. If the appraisal system is carried out properly with set goals then the situation should become obvious to both the appraiser and the appraisee. Any criticism needs to be specific sticking to facts and describing consequences, both as far as the process is concerned and specifically about the outcomes. Try not to discuss everything in terms in judgement of behaviour such as 'you are lazy' or 'you are domineering'. An emotional attack is usually countered and becomes very hard for either to change or to compromise without losing face. With facts, explore alternatives and try to keep things moving, drawing threads together, recapping and restating to get agreement and also recording them.

ARROGANCE

Arrogance is linked with authoritarianism which can be useful and indeed necessary in some situations. An arrogant person usually feels that if another person's perception is different from theirs, then that person must be wrong. They are often complacent resulting from a difficulty in perceiving that they have anything to learn. It may also be a cover-up for self-doubt.

Feedback has to be from somebody they feel is credible and possibly someone senior to them or another external third party such as a management consultant. They often have problems with evidence-based medicine because it may involve a change in their practice and an understanding that other people may know better than they do and this could undermine their self-confidence.

They have got to distinguish between being competent and being boastful. They should be asked to supervise senior people, so that they have to receive and discuss feedback from them. When they do perform in public, anonymous feedback can be obtained from the audience. They must be helped to see that their authoritarian nature or arrogance actually undermines their reputation and makes people think less well of them.

85

DISCRIMINATORY PRACTICE

The attitudes and behaviour of some may fall short of equality standards leading to unrest and disharmony. Directorates and departments need to be managed in the full spirit of equal opportunities, with respect for religious and cultural origin and avoidance of bias on the basis of age, gender or disability.

Any suggestion of discrimination must be addressed and resolved in the same manner as any other attitudinal issue, using the eight point formula (see page 76). Anti-discriminatory practice is enshrined in legislation, and if the issue cannot be resolved quickly advice should be sought from the personnel department.

ORGANISATION AND RESOURCE ISSUES

It is important to state that even the most highly motivated, focused and competent teams may not achieve their objectives in the face of significant organisational constraints. Underperformance may be due to the conditions under which people work, including inadequate resources in terms of personnel or equipment. It may be that the expected level of performance was unrealistic within the resources obtainable, and so the reasons for underperformance lie not with the individual or even departments but must be addressed by the organisation as a whole.

The purpose of appraisal is to help assure that management, the workforce, resources and training strategy are aligned. Those being appraised have responsibility to deliver on their objectives and therefore have a genuine grievance if these cannot be achieved because of lack of commitment from management. This is why the role of the appraiser is so important as he is a vital link in the management process. The appraiser must therefore be well prepared for the appraisal interview and have anticipated (and where possible negotiated) the resource implications of any new targets for the individual appraisee.

If there is no such empowerment then the appraisal becomes a totally meaningless paper exercise. It must be a genuine two-way process leading to what is, in effect, a contract and should be enforceable. The appraisee has a right to expect that if they do come to a decision and particularly if there have been compromises, that it will be honoured. If there is no such empowerment then in reality the process becomes dishonest and very quickly will fall into disrepute, being seen only as a means of gaining control of the workforce.

The appraisee has also the right to expect that the appraiser has been trained in the appraisal process and is genuinely committed to it. It is therefore important that feedback is obtained from those being appraised as regards to both the process and the outcomes of the appraisal system and that there is a genuine partnership between management and staff. If not, then instead of producing personnel who are motivated and eager to obtain a result of behalf of the patients, themselves and the organisation, then the reverse becomes true with demoralization resulting in decreasing clinical standards.

FOLLOW-UP

Follow-up and two-way feedback is essential. Once potential solutions are identified, a system of measurement must be put in place to monitor progress. The monitoring may be achieved through personal observation, exam or course results or reports from colleagues. Also, a record should be kept of whether and when any follow-up appraisal is required.

THE APPEAL PROCESS

If agreement cannot be reached and the issue is sufficiently important or serious enough it is best to involve a third party to try and resolve it. The question is whether or not the objective is reasonable and attainable and particularly if it has been achieved by others with good results. If so, the appraiser should try and ascertain directly from the individual why they are objecting, and finally a decision must be taken whether the objective is sufficiently important for it to be achieved in full or whether there is room for compromise.

Occasionally, the objections are not to do with the issue but more resentment that the appraiser has brought the matter up and the appraisee feels that the appraiser is either too young or not sufficiently qualified to deal with the matter. Again, the exact grounds for disagreement with the objective should be sought. The appraiser should try not to be defensive and simply state facts such as 'I have researched this and have discussed the issue with other senior colleagues and I am clear on the facts. I have tried my best to work with you to resolve the matter. If we cannot agree we must involve a third party to resolve this important matter. Ultimately we must reach an acceptable solution. Failure to do so could result in disciplinary action'.

The appeal therefore is to a higher authority within the organisation or, especially with professionals, to an external source. Both parties must commit to accepting the results of the appeal process.

If the appraisee fails to accept the resolved advice of an appropriate authority then management must govern, and disciplinary proceedings instigated in full conjunction with personnel colleagues who will advise on the process. The appraisee must receive a written notification of the problem, why it is important and what the consequences are both for the individual and the organisation if the matter is not addressed. Disciplinary action must be clearly seen to be a totally separate process from the appraisal system. However, once proceedings are instituted, reference will be made to the fact that the problem was identified as part of the continuing process of appraisal and, in spite of grievance and appeal, no changes occurred. Records of conversations during the appraisal should not to be used as evidence in the disciplinary procedure. However the personal development plan and decisions made may well attest to the facts and relative merits of the case.

CONCLUSION

However effective the appraisal process, it is inevitable that from time to time there will be issues and difficulties which inhibit achievement of the individual's personal development plan and *de facto* the achievement of departmental targets. These should be addressed promptly and sensitively with due respect for the views of the clinician concerned.

The focus should be on the overall objectives of the organisation and on patient care. While there should be tolerance for different clinicians having different approaches and methods, all must work within agreed policies and procedures and to agreed standards - both clinical and ethical.

Any problems that arise need to be clearly and objectively defined. Usually it should be possible to resolve issues and agree the way forward, either between the two parties or assisted by someone peripheral to the process. When this is not possible the matter should be formally referred to an appeal mechanism which is respected by both sides, who must agree to accept the conclusions.

In rare situations where there is continued and unjustified resistance to change, it will be necessary to set out the consequences for the individual and the organisation and to recommend disciplinary procedures. While appraisal and disciplinary processes are quite separate, clearly evidence from the appraisal process that demonstrates breaches of agreement or failure to address concerns, may be used in disciplinary action. Similarly, evidence of good practice and achievement of previous objectives can be considered in defence of the appraisee's position.

88 At the end of the day, by cooperation, collaboration or compromise, it is to be hoped that there will be satisfactory resolution. Confrontation cannot be avoided in all cases but should only be seen as a last resort unless there are implications for patient care. The situation is best avoided by training and education at all levels within the organisation and continuing dialogue between all parties.

chapter 9
INTEGRATING APPRAISAL INTO OPERATIONAL MANAGEMENT

INTRODUCTION

STRATEGIC MANAGEMENT is about setting the direction of an organisation within political, social and economic constraints. This sets overall aims and goals which then must be operationalised within the various sub-units or departments.

The hallmark of a successful organisation is that it is proactive and not reactive. The crucial role of management is to plan in some detail for the achievement of the organisational objectives and to ensure that the plan is carried through.

ORGANISATIONAL PLAN

FIG.1 ORGANISATIONAL PLANNING

Operational management translates the strategic plan into clear objectives with specific timescales, checking that these are achieved and providing feedback to the organisation in order to inform future strategic planning. It is also responsible for maintaining core functions and identifying developmental needs including resources and training.

The Appraisal System is a key method by which operational management produces action on the ground in as cost efficient manner as possible. The formula linking cost efficiency, output, workforce and the resources is as follows:

$$\text{Cost Efficiency} = \frac{Vo}{Qo} \left\{ \frac{Cw \times Aw}{Nw} + \frac{Qr}{Fr} \right\}$$

where:

A = attitude	Q = quality
C = competence	R = resource
F = fixed costs	W = workforce
N = number	V = volume
O = output	

It can be seen from the above that cost efficiency can be altered and balanced in a number of ways; this is the function of operational management. For example, efficiency may be increased by raising the competence and commitment of the workforce or by decreasing the numbers involved or the fixed costs. Appraisal is a basic tool for turning the objectives into action, through the proper use of human resources.

PRODUCING AND ALLOCATING OBJECTIVES

The first step for management is to take the overall strategic plan and determine those specific areas of responsibility for each clinical directorate and each department. They must also clarify issues such as the resources available to the department including the finance.

Figure 1 represents the overall responsibilities of a department. These need to be prioritised and allocated, usually by undertaking a risk assessment and weighting the various parameters. The next step is to assess the personnel in the department, identifying their strengths and weaknesses as well as their likes and dislikes. Based on this, the responsibility for as many of the objectives as possible is then allocated to key personnel. This exercise exposes any gaps in the provision of the service. These need to be discussed within the department and a plan formulated for dealing with the outstanding issues.

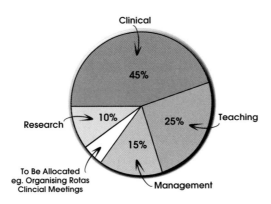

FIG.2 APPORTIONING DEPARTMENTAL RESPONSIBILITIES

This may require negotiation with individuals to encourage them to take on an extra workload. A *quid pro quo* is important and as far as possible any solution should be negotiated and not imposed. At the end of the day there is a bottom line and, within reason, some solutions may have to be imposed. Reasonableness is the key since any change imposed is liable to be opposed, and alienating the workforce is not the best way to achieve quality results. Developmental and any consequent training needs must be identified and resources allocated to deal with them at this time. Once agreements are reached, these form the basis for negotiating personal development plans for staff during the appraisal process with the outcomes clearly documented in terms of SMART (specific, measurable, achievable, relevant and timely) objectives.

What happens if there is a sudden change in departmental responsibilities during the appraisal period? The appraisal system helps management as they can look at the current job description and personal development plans and come to agreement about any change that is required. This again is a negotiated process, with robust objective and priority setting. It should be quite easy to determine what may be dropped or altered if there is a well-documented personal development plan by looking at the likely consequences of moving to a new set of objectives. Everything is a matter of stating priorities, undertaking risk assessment and acknowledging the expertise of the workforce, who should be involved in the negotiating process. Professionals who feel involved are much more likely to be motivated towards achieving the results, and it is they at the end of the day who maintain the high quality output.

Objectives must be risk weighted. This is not just looking at the level of risk but other elements such as priorities and timelines, so that these are reviewed at the appropriate time. For instance, in the process of development some activities or equipment have to be in place before further stages can be reached. There is no point in waiting a year to find these basic steps have not been carried out. In other words, checkpoints are essential along the way in order to keep the process moving. Also, objectives may need to be updated throughout the year because of new knowledge and different priorities that develop in the light of experience.

92 PERSONNEL

In relation to the Health Service, the role of the Medical Director, the Clinical Director and the Lead Clinicians as operational managers is particularly valuable. They have been fully trained within the system, and are usually practicing clinicians with direct responsibility for patient care. Therefore, they are uniquely placed to observe and comment on the impact of management decisions, which they have helped to make, on both patients and professional staff. They provide a solid basis for good communication between the medical staff and the non-clinical Executive Management Group, ensuring strategic decision-making is bedded in operational reality.

It becomes immediately obvious that management, such as the Clinical Directors, must know individuals and teams, their strengths and weaknesses, their likes and dislikes and what training issues are around so that the best use can be made within the overall plan. An appraisal system, based on discussion and mutual respect is essential to help a department move forward, helping people to grow and develop rather than giving the appearance of being management interference and continuing examination of every aspect of a professional's practice.

Central to all of this is attitude, relating to both that of the Clinical Directors and those within the department. If everyone is forward-looking and willingly on side, it is much easier to sort out any problems that arise. Resistance or discontent can very quickly negate any plan and hamper the performance of a department.

PERFORMANCE APPRAISAL

This is essential if operational or strategic management is going to work at all. The important function of management is therefore to develop the appraisal system, by deciding what approach is going to be used, how and where it is going to be introduced, who exactly is going to be covered by it and whether it is going to be the same for everyone. Whatever else it is, it must be seen to be fair.

Time must be spent on developing the process. This means taking the best advice available, understanding the performance management process and how the outcomes are documented. Following consultation with all involved, there should be a pilot scheme with evaluation and feedback both from the appraisers and appraisees as well as the management. By the time the appraisal system is put into operation there must be a clear statement of the objectives and of the benefits to both personnel and the organisation. It is essential not simply to lift one 'off the shelf' and implement it immediately. Individual circumstances can vary quite considerably and what is essential in one department may not be the same in another. The process should be amended accordingly before full implementation.

93

Everyone involved will require training and guidance in the process, including the appraisees. There is a need to understand the nature and use of objectives, competencies, the type of programme and the development plan to be used, method of conducting the appraisal and how the discussions are going to be held. Everyone needs to understand the nature of the records that are to be maintained and particularly how they are going to be stored specifically with regards to confidentiality. It needs to be seen as a positive benefit with promotion of personal development and with guarantees that any decisions will be backed by resources. Otherwise the whole process will soon become a paper exercise and fall into disrepute.

CONCLUSION

The appraisal system is one of the main tools of operational management. It is a method whereby what is actually happening in reality on a day-to-day basis is assessed by operational managers and fed back to strategic management. Without such a system, a lot of outcomes are left to chance and difficulties are not identified and dealt with at any early stage.

Accordingly it is essential that all professionals are fully involved in the planning, development and implementation phases of the appraisal system so that they have ownership and see the benefits of active participation. An imposed one-way system whereby professionals see themselves at the bottom of the pile leads to demoralisation and demotivation. Most medical staff are dedicated to their work and are keen to produce a high quality service for their patients. It is therefore vital that they feel that the process allows them to act as sensors on the ground, feeding back to all levels of management in a manner that clearly influences the direction of the organisation. Only then will they produce the energy that to drive the organisation forward and ensure high quality care.

chapter 10
INTRODUCING APPRAISAL FOR SENIOR STAFF

INTRODUCTION

THIS CHAPTER OUTLINES the process for the introduction of an appraisal system where none has existed before. Such a programme represents a culture change within the organisation and it can be very disconcerting or even threatening for established senior staff. Perhaps for the first time, they are being questioned about their performance and competence, asked to set targets for themselves and their department and be held accountable for achieving them.

Getting off to a good start is obviously important and yet it is unlikely that these changes can be introduced without some level of opposition or at least robust questioning of the concept. Some resistance may be due to quite reasonably held beliefs, but undoubtedly part of the opposition is due to a fear of the unknown. The situation needs to be handled sensitively and, as with managing any change process, needs to involve all of the stakeholders to create ownership of the developments.

This chapter revolves around a 10-point plan for the introduction of peer appraisal.

OUTLINE SCHEME

Formation of a steering group.

Seminar for all involved personnel.

Appointment of appraisers.

Training appraisers.

Training for appraisees.

Setting the agenda for first interview.

Piloting the appraisal cycle.

Evaluation of feedback by steering group.

Further discussion with the staff.

Implementation plan.

Each point will now be discussed in greater detail.

FORMATION OF A STEERING GROUP

It is important that people on the steering group are known to, and well respected by, the permanent staff. Membership should include representatives from all the directorates, both clinical and support staff, as well as a senior manager and a senior representative from the personnel department. It is important that they are committed to the concept of an appraisal system and are prepared to devote their time to developing the system and their energy into providing leadership for their colleagues to overcome any obstacles.

The steering group will usually be usually be chaired by the Medical Director, but may be chaired by a Lead Clinician with a specific interest in appraisal.

SEMINAR FOR ALL INVOLVED PERSONNEL

It is vital that from the beginning that all feel involved with the programme and eventually take ownership of it. The seminar should provide the rationale behind the introduction of appraisal, perhaps giving examples of what has been happening elsewhere. The benefits to both themselves and the organisation should be stressed.

The discussion is structured so as to obtain maximum contribution from the staff, particularly encouraging them to highlight any areas of concern. They should be assured that all their concerns will be taken on board by the steering group and that their views will be actively sought throughout the development phase.

APPOINTMENT OF APPRAISERS

One of the keys to a successful appraisal system is the selection of credible and committed appraisers who have good interpersonal skills and are committed to developing expertise within the appraisal process (chapter 5). Like the steering group they must have the respect of their peers.

TRAINING APPRAISERS

A sample programme with two half-day workshops as run by the Royal College of Surgeons of England is included at the end of this chapter as Appendix B. The first module covers types of assessment, the elements of a personal development plan and how to define objectives. It also introduces discussion on the nature of the appraisal interview and how to give positive feedback. At the end of the module, some specific tasks are set for module two which consists of defining the appraisers' own job descriptions and roles and asks them to think about specific objectives for themselves over the coming year.

The second module develops further the production of personal development plans and discusses how to gather the information required. There is a section dealing with difficult issues and a role-play of an appraisal interview is included.

TRAINING FOR APPRAISEES

A sample programme of a half-day workshop is also included as Appendix B, to help appraisees fully understand the appraisal process, and in particular how it can be of benefit to them. This format facilitates open discussion during which concerns may be raised and resolved.

Participants are shown how to develop a personal portfolio, and how this is used in the appraisal interview, by coupling with the setting of clear objectives to construct a personal development plan.

SETTING THE AGENDA FOR THE FIRST INTERVIEW

Experience has shown that prior to the introduction of an appraisal system there is often a lack of clarity about the details of an individual's job description and role. The first appraisal interview should therefore concentrate on agreeing the core elements and objectives of the job, to set a clear baseline that is unequivocally understood by all parties. Therefore, the main item on the agenda for the first interview will be the clarification of the job description and role and this will take up most of the time.

When compiling the draft agenda, the appraiser will also suggest one or two specific items and invite the appraisee to add items they wish to discuss. It is important that the agenda is restricted to a manageable number of topics.

PILOTING THE APPRAISAL CYCLE

In order to test the process, each appraiser will undertake two or three appraisal interviews, probably with the more senior staff. On completion, there should be a clearly written job description and role with several personal development targets for the coming year. Following this, feedback should be actively sought from the senior people who were appraised covering all facets of the process. They should also be invited to give feedback to the appraiser to help them refine their technique.

EVALUATION OF FEEDBACK BY STEERING GROUP

This represents an opportunity for the various stakeholders to reflect on the process. They identify the aspects that worked well as well as considering and planning how to resolve any outstanding difficulties.

98 ## FURTHER DISCUSSIONS WITH STAFF

Once the system has been piloted, the feedback obtained and adjustments made as necessary, there should be one final meeting with all staff. This is to inform them of the definitive cycle, to take any more comments and to organise for full implementation.

IMPLEMENTATION PLAN

All staff are now involved. Agreement should be reached within each directorate as to who is responsible for appraising whom and the detail of the timescale required for achieving the first round of appraisal interviews.

CONCLUSION

The introduction of an effective appraisal system requires a commitment from the organisation, a clear process and good communication with involvement of all the stakeholders. While the process should not be rushed, the pace should be measured. The 10-step plan outlined above can be implemented within a period of three to four months.

Training is essential for both appraisers and appraisees and details of a modular course offered by the Royal College of Surgeons are included. Most of the information necessary to run these modules is included within the chapters of this book.

APPENDIX "A"

ABC HEALTH TRUST

APPRAISAL FORM AND PERSONAL DEVELOPMENT PLAN

Date of Appraisal Interview: _____   Period Under Review: _____

Name: _____   Date of Birth: _____

Qualifications: _____   Date on Specialist Register: _____

Grade: _____ (No. of Sessions _____)   Date of Appointment: _____

Distinction Award Level: _____   Proof of Current CME: _____

(Per Specialist Association)

COMPLAINTS / DISCIPLINARY ACTION

Date: _____

Outcome:

_____

_____

_____

Pending:

_____

_____

_____

Special Circumstances

_____

_____

_____

ABC HEALTH TRUST

APPRAISAL FORM AND PERSONAL DEVELOPMENT PLAN

Name: ——————————————— Period Under Review: ————————

PLEASE REVIEW UNDER THE FOLLOWING HEADINGS:

100

1. What has been achieved?

———————————————————————————————————————

———————————————————————————————————————

2. What problem has been overcome?

———————————————————————————————————————

———————————————————————————————————————

3. What has not been fully achieved?

———————————————————————————————————————

———————————————————————————————————————

4. Why?

———————————————————————————————————————

———————————————————————————————————————

5. What objectives should be set for the next period?

———————————————————————————————————————

———————————————————————————————————————

6. What are the Supervision, Training and Resource implications?

———————————————————————————————————————

———————————————————————————————————————

ABC HEALTH TRUST

APPRAISAL FORM AND PERSONAL DEVELOPMENT PLAN

Name: _____   Period Under Review: _____

OBJECTIVE	PRIORITY	STANDARD	TIME SCALE IMPLICATIONS	TRAINING NEEDS	RESOURCE	
1. Introduce Appraisal system for Trust	High	As per GMC guidelines	6 months (give specific date)	1. Attend Appraisal Course	**Direct**	
				2. Visit XYZ Trust to discuss implementation	Course/Travel	£1,000
					Workbooks for staff	£1,000
				3. Arrangements for Monitoring	Secretarial	£5,000 (ongoing)
					Indirect	
				4. Two In-house Training Courses for Lead Clinicians	Personal:	1 session/week
					Staff: Lead clinicians	2 sessions/month
				Consultants		1 session/month
				5. One In-house Training Courses for other staff		
2. Reduce waiting list for inguinal hernia repair to 3 months	High	National guidelines for day procedure units	(Specific date)	Nil Specific	Within available resources	
3.						

APPENDIX "B"

The Royal College *of* Surgeons *of* England

APPRAISAL AND ASSESSMENT WORKSHOP

MODULE 1 – *for Appraisers*

Course Convenor - Mr Rodney Peyton

8.30 - 8.45 am   **Registration and Coffee**

8.45 - 9.15 am   **1. WELCOME AND INTRODUCTIONS**

Objectives:

- to overview this programme and its purposes
- to identify specific wants and needs of participants

9.15 - 10.00 am   **2. ASSESSMENT, APPRAISAL AND EVALUATION**

Objectives:

- to understand the terms Assessment, Appraisal and Evaluation
- to understand the purposes of each
- to define the basic concepts of Validity, Reliability, Feasibility and Fidelity

10.00 - 10.45 am   **3. TYPES OF ASSESSMENT**

Objectives:

- to understand the principals of Criteria based, Norm based, Self based and Limen based assessments
- to discuss the pros and cons of each
- to identify the elements of a Consultants work plan
- to link work plans with personal and local healthcare objectives

10.45 - 11.00 am   *Coffee*

11.00 - 11.45 am   **4. THE PROCESS OF APPRAISAL AND ASSESSMENT**

Objectives:

- to develop a coherent strategy including the key elements of preparation, interview and follow up
- to understand the fundamental importance of having clearly defined objectives
- to discuss how to define and gather the information required

11.45 - 12.15 pm   **5. THE APPRAISAL / ASSESSMENT INTERVIEW**

Objectives:

- to make the interview a concise and empowering episode for appraised and appraiser
- to define the competencies required of a good appraiser
- to give positive feedback
- to produce a Personal Development Plan

12.15 - 12.45 pm   **6. SUMMARY AND NEXT STEPS**

Objectives:

- to recap the key messages from the module
- to discuss the implications of these for appraising and assessing the workforce
- to set specific tasks for Module 2
- to decide the format of feedback and reporting in Module 2

12.45 - 1.00 pm   **7. CLOSURE**

Objectives:

- to give feedback on the content of the module
- to discuss how this programme meets the needs and wants of the participants as identified in the session
- to suggest improvements

The Royal College *of* Surgeons *of* England

APPRAISAL AND ASSESSMENT WORKSHOP

MODULE 2 – *for Appraisers*

Course Convenor - Mr Rodney Peyton

8.30 - 8.45 am   **Registration and Coffee**

8.45 - 9.30 am   **1. INTRODUCTION**

Objectives:

- to review the main points from module one and clarify any issues
- to review the feedback from module one and add specific points for discussion during module two

9.30 - 10.30 am   **2. THE APPRAISAL INTERVIEW – SET UP**

Objectives:

- to formulate a clear personal development plan
- to understand the process of setting up an assessment interview
- to discuss the gathering of material in order to give feedback.
- to learn one method of giving feedback to a professional colleague

10.30 - 10.45 am   *Coffee*

10.45 - 11.30 am   **3. DEALING WITH DIFFICULT ISSUES**

Objectives:

- to air, discuss and decide on methods of dealing with difficulties arising with resources or personalities

11.30 - 12.30 pm   **4. THE APPRAISAL INTERVIEW – ROLE PLAY**

Objectives:

- to set up a run three short interviews
- to discuss the outcomes and decide on a system to operate locally

12.30 - 1.00 pm   **5. NOW DO IT!**

Objectives:

- to formulate a plan for implementing the appraisal system
- to give feedback on Module 2

APPRAISAL AND ASSESSMENT WORKSHOP

MODULE 3 – *for Appraisees*

Course Convenor - Mr Rodney Peyton

8.45- 9.00 am **Registration and Coffee**

9.00 - 9.15 am **1. WELCOME AND INTRODUCTIONS**

Objectives:
- to overview this programme and its purposes
- to outline the appraisal system for the trust

9.15 - 9.30 am **2. WHY APPRAISE AND ASSESS?**

Objectives:
- to understand the terms Appraisal, Assessment and Evaluation
- to understand the purposes of appraisal
- to discuss the benefits of appraisal for individual clinicians

9.30 - 10.00 am **3. PROBLEMS WITH APPRAISAL**

Objectives:
- to identify specific problems relevant to participants
- to understand the reasons why these issues are regarded as problematical

10.00 - 10.30 am **4. ADDRESSING DIFFICULT ISSUES**

Objectives:
- to discuss the issues raised in serial 3
- to achieve resolution of perceived problems

10.30 - 10.45 am *Coffee*

10.45 - 11.30 am **5. THE APPRAISAL PROCESS**

Objectives:
- to understand the appraisal cycle
- to detail the elements of each step in the process
- to discuss the personal portfolio and production of a Personal Development Plan
- to understand the nature of the appraisal interview

11.30 - 11.45 am **6. OPEN DISCUSSION**

Objectives:
- to obtain feedback from participants on the appraisal process
- to resolve any outstanding issues

11.45 - 12.00 noon **7. CLOSURE**

Objectives:
- to receive feedback on the content of the module
- to suggest improvements to the programme

INDEX

108

109

Coming soon!

Three new titles in the Medical Education Series

COMMUNICATION IN MEDICAL PRACTICE - *spring 2001*

Very little in the way of communication skills is taught and yet, knowing how to adequately communicate with patients, peers and the public is becoming increasingly important. This book includes such matters as dealing with patient confidentiality, breaking bad news and handling complaints; giving talks and papers to peers including the use of tele-medicine, and dealing with 'whistle blowing'; how to handle the media and give evidence in Court and how to reflect on practice to set objectives and deal with personal communication issues.

STUDY TECHNIQUES FOR SUCCESSFUL ADULT LEARNING - *summer 2001*

We now recognise that we must all be committed to lifelong learning. Adults learn differently than children because of the application of experience and knowledge. However, very few adult learners have taken the time to understand how they best learn. In addition to a discussion on how adults learn and an account of individual study techniques, the book gives the reader the opportunity to carry out a self-assessment using questionnaires and MCQ's which are used to assist the reader in understanding more about their own learning style and how to apply and make the most of it.

AVOIDING LITIGATION IN MEDICAL PRACTICE: MEDICINE, ETHICS AND THE LAW - *autumn 2001*

The National Health Service is being overwhelmed with medical negligence claims, the cost of which is diverting financial resources away from patient care. At the same time, current medical practice is placing a significant legal burden on doctors in relation to their handling of matters such as the living will, informed consent and confidentiality. This book is not a book for solicitors but a practical book for doctors written by doctors explaining the ground rules of the law as it relates to medical litigation. In particular, it provides suggestions on prevention: how to avoid making the mistakes which may lead to costly, time-consuming and unnecessary litigation. For those who wish to act as an expert witness, the book provides a detailed account of writing reports, giving evidence and how to get paid for the service.

MANTICORE EUROPE LTD FREEPOST ANG0424 RICKMANSWORTH HERTS WD3 5WD

Please send me more information about your future publications in your Medical Education series:

Communication in Medical Practice ❑

Study Techniques for Successful Adult Learning ❑

Avoiding Litigation in Medical Practice: Medicine, Ethics and the Law ❑

Name: . . . .

Address: . . . .

. . . .

. . . .

. . . .